**FOR THE
FIRST TIME
IN PAPERBACK**

112 CHALLENGING QUIZZES
to test your backgammon skills,
plus ground rules and strategies
for all types of play, including:

warm-up quizzes
the opening game
hitting plays
the back game
the middle game
when the opponent is on the bar
the prime
various positional plays
end-game plays
bearing off

THE BACKGAMMON QUIZ BOOK

BY PRINCE JOLI KANSIL
tournament expert, teacher and writer

*"A thoroughly enjoyable and relaxing way to sharpen
your game and learn to think as an expert does."*

Oswald Jacoby

THE BACKGAMMON QUIZ BOOK

BY PRINCE JOLI KANSIL
WITH A FOREWORD BY OSWALD JACOBY

PLAYBOY PRESS
PAPERBACKS

In Memory of
ALBERT H. MOREHEAD and
JOHN R. CRAWFORD

THE BACKGAMMON QUIZ BOOK

Copyright © 1978 by Prince Joli Kansil.

Published simultaneously in the United States and Canada by Playboy Press, Chicago, Illinois. Printed in the United States of America. Library of Congress Catalog Card Number: 78-59969. First edition.

Books are available at quantity discounts for promotional and industrial use. For further information, write our sales-promotion agency: Ventura Associates, 40 East 49th Street, New York, New York 10017.

ISBN: 0-872-16491-8

CONTENTS

FOREWORD

Some twenty-odd backgammon books have been published since the game reached craze proportions in the 1970s, and except for *The Backgammon Book* by John Crawford and me, and a few other works, these books have been geared solely for the beginner. The need for more literature for players with experience at the game has been acute and *The Backgammon Quiz Book* by Prince Joli Kansil helps to fill this void. The format employed in this book proves to be a thoroughly enjoyable and relaxing way for the backgammon enthusiast at all levels not only to sharpen his game but to learn to *think* as an expert does.

Twelve years ago, I knew Prince Joli Kansil as a young college bridge whiz who had just invented Bridgette, which I have called the greatest two-handed bridge game ever devised. Since then he has created many other games, a slew of crossword puzzles for *The New York Times* and his own system of backgammon notation. Kansil Backgammon Notation has made it easy, at last, to read a backgammon diagram, and it is the only system designed that can be used to record a backgammon game as it is played—no matter how quickly the players move their men.

The quiz problems that are in this volume are not freakish puzzles; they are practical situations that occur frequently in actual games. I would hasten to mention that players who master the concepts dealt with in *The Backgammon Quiz Book* cannot help but seriously improve their skills at backgammon.

I hope you have as much fun trying to solve these quizzes as I have had!

— OSWALD JACOBY

Dallas
July 26, 1978

INTRODUCTION

Basic Ground Rules

In all of the backgammon quizzes in these pages, you, the reader, play the White pieces and move in a counterclockwise direction toward the lower right corner of the board. Each quiz has three parts: It is your turn in each and you must figure out the best possible play for each of the three dice rolls given. You may want to actually set up the diagramed situation on your own backgammon board so that you can try different moves before selecting your final choice.

All the quizzes deal with teaching you how to move the men most effectively. The doubling cube is ignored. Admittedly the cube accounts for 30 to 40 percent of the skill factor in backgammon, but its use is learned through experience and judgment rather than "by the book." You will find that experts are rarely unanimous in their opinion of when to offer a double or when to accept or refuse one. But in moving the men, they are more often than not in accord in recommending one play over an alternative play.

There are many outside factors that come into play in deciding one move over another: how strong or weak your opponent is, how freely he gives or takes doubles, what the stake is or what the score in the match is, and various subtle psychological factors. To avoid adding all of these other ingredients into these quizzes, you should envision that you are playing against an opponent of approximately equal skill and temperament and that the problem shown is occurring during the very first game of your match.

Kansil Backgammon Notation

Once you decide your choice of play, you indicate your move by simply recording it on the line immediately below the two dice shown by using letters A to Z. In the Sample Quiz (see page 15), you must indicate your responses to your opponent's opening 6-2 play with three different dice rolls: 3-1, double 1 and 5-2. In the first case, 3-1, if you think you should make your 5-point, you would note this by writing RU TU on the line; if, alternatively, you feel you should hit your opponent's blot, you would write B–F'. A *dash* is used to note that *one man is moved more than one number on the dice* and, thus, such man touches down at some point in between; an *apostrophe* is used to indicate that the *opponent's blot is hit*. Note that the play B–F' could also be recorded BEF' or BCF'.

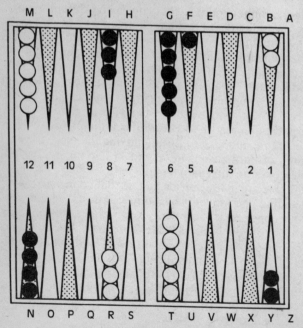

Now go on to the second example, double 1. If you feel that instead of hitting you should make your 5-point and 7-point (bar-point), you would record the following on the line: RS2 TU2. The number 2 means that two men are moved together.

In the third situation, you must play a roll of 5-2. If you would play this throw by bringing down two men from your opponent's 12-point, you would write MR MO to indicate this play. Only after you have completed recording your choices for all three dice rolls do you check your answers by turning the page and reading the explanations.

In some examples, you have to enter a man from the bar. You indicate this by using the letter A. For example, AB would mean that you enter on your opponent's 1-point. In the diagram below, if your roll were 3-1, you

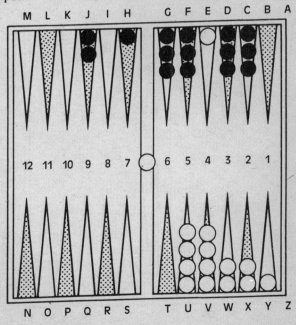

would play A–E (A "to" E), making your opponent's 4-point. If your roll were 6-4, you would play A–K. (Remember that a dash is used to indicate that you touched down at some intervening point.) If your roll were 6-1, you would record your play A–H' ("A to H, hit"). A short line (—) is used to signify that one of your dice is unplayable or that you have two men on the bar and can enter only one of them. In the diagram on page 11, you would play a roll of 5-4 by writing AE —. To record bearing off a man, you use the letter Z. Thus, in the diagram below, UZ XZ means you bore off a man from your 5-point and from your 2-point with a roll of 6-2 or 5-2. If you rolled 4-1 instead, you could bear off by hitting (UV'Z) or by not hitting (UYZ), and here you should clearly indicate your choice by using the intervening letter, not by using a dash (U–Z). Sometimes

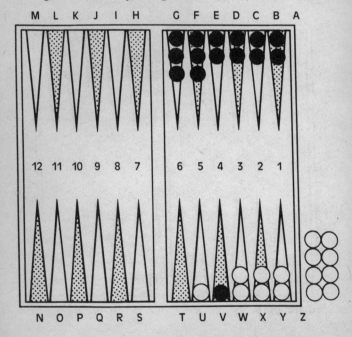

doubles can be indicated in more than one way. To illustrate, an opening roll of double 5 is best recorded as M–W2, but it would not be incorrect to write it as MRW2 or M–W MR RW. As long as the way you have moved is the same as given in the solution, that is all that counts. After you have completed a few of the quizzes, you will observe the recommended preferences in recording. As a further way of familiarizing yourself with Kansil Backgammon Notation, look at page 271 of the Appendix and you will see all of the suggested ways for playing the opening rolls notated in KBN.

Keeping Score

These quizzes are designed as a learning experience to improve your backgammon; it is not necessary to keep track of how many you answer "right" or "wrong." But, if you do wish to keep score to see how well you have done, you earn five points if your answer agrees with the suggested solution. Fewer points are given for alternative answers that have merit and that amount is indicated above each explanation. The maximum you can score for each quiz is 15. There are eight quizzes in each section and after you have finished a section, you can add your eight scores and record the total on the first page of the section in the space provided. You can use this total to rank yourself for the whole section as follows:

100 or higher . . . . Tournament Grandmaster
90-99 . . . . .Club Champion
80-89 . . . . Very Good
70-79 . . . . .Good
60-69 . . . . .Fair

For any particular quiz, a total score of 12 or higher is superior.

Some Final Words

The five sections of Basic Quizzes are designed for novices—advanced beginners and average intermediate players—but even players who would rate

13

themselves at a higher skill level will find these quizzes quite informative. The nine sections of Advanced Quizzes contain much new material that has not appeared in previous works on backgammon. Readers may not agree with the suggested solution for each quiz, but it is hoped they will at least appreciate the logic of the explanation given. I like to use the phrase "suggested solution" instead of "correct solution," for often one or more alternatives are all sound plays.

A number of prominent international backgammon experts and local members of the Honolulu Backgammon Club played a role in reviewing most of these quizzes and offering needed revisions. Special thanks goes to four individuals in particular: Oswald Jacoby, one of the great bridge, gin rummy, poker, canasta and backgammon players for the last 50 years; Dennis Stone, playwright and a semifinalist at the 1977 Amateur Backgammon Championship in Las Vegas; Lyn Goldsmith, a protégée of Paul Magriel and recognized by many as the top woman backgammon player in the world; and Waldemar von Zedtwitz, one of the greatest bridge players of all time and an expert at chess and backgammon problems.

Best of luck in solving these quizzes.

PRINCE JOLI KANSIL

Kerambitan Village, Bali
(Indonesia)
December 6, 1977

SAMPLE QUIZ

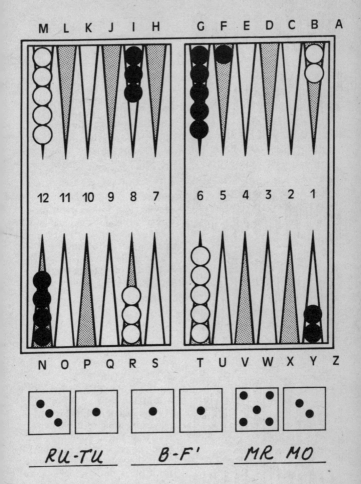

RU-TU   B-F'   MR MO

SCORE _12_

15

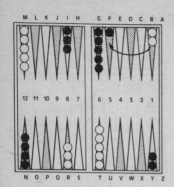

3-1   RU TU=3
BC MP=1

B–F'

Hitting Black's blot is more
important than making your
5-point. By sending your
opponent to the bar, you push
him back 20 pips and you also
give yourself an anchor for
making your opponent's 5-point.
If your roll had been 4-2, you
would also elect to hit.

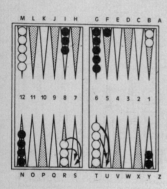

1-1   B–F'=4

RS2 TU2

Making your 5-point and 7-point
(bar-point) is just too good to
pass up. This is your best
opening roll and it must be
played to the maximum — even
at the risk of ignoring Black's
blot on his key 5-point.

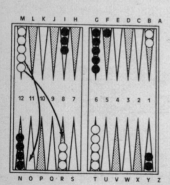

5-2   BD MR=2
MR TV=2

MR MO

As an opening roll, 5-2 is best
played by bringing down two
men from the 12-point
(mid-point). Splitting your back
men, alternatively, is too daring,
for if Black throws double 5, he
will pounce on both your blots
and make two points besides.

BASIC QUIZZES

I
THE OPENING GAME

SCORE FOR THIS SECTION 77 - 1/2

1

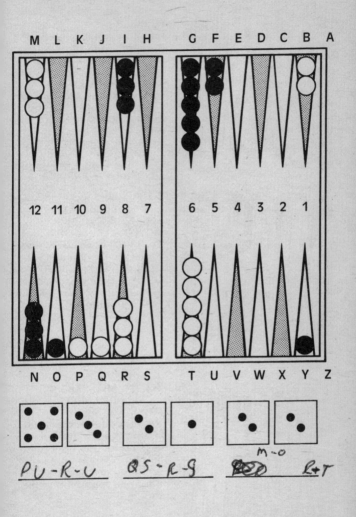

PU - R - U   QS - R - g   ~~PQD~~   m-o   R+T

SCORE 8

19

5-3 RW TW=2
MP TY'=1

PU RU

One of the reasons for bringing down builders to your 9-point and 10-point is that it will be easy to make your key defensive points. This roll is a good one and should be used to make your 5-point. Your 3-point could also be made (RW TW), but it is not nearly so valuable.

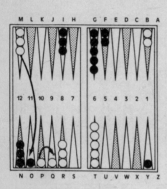

2-1 QS RS=3
BC MO'=1
B–E=1

MO' PQ

You should hit and make your 9-point and thus give yourself a strong attacking position. Playing QS RS to make your 7-point has merit, but this position calls for a more aggressive play.

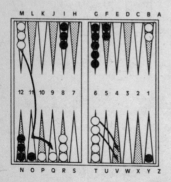

2-2 MO'–S QS=4
BD2 MO'Q=2

MO'Q TV2

You must hit. The question is whether to make your 7-point or your 4-point. The 4-point looks a little better as you begin to strengthen your inner board while your opponent is on the bar.

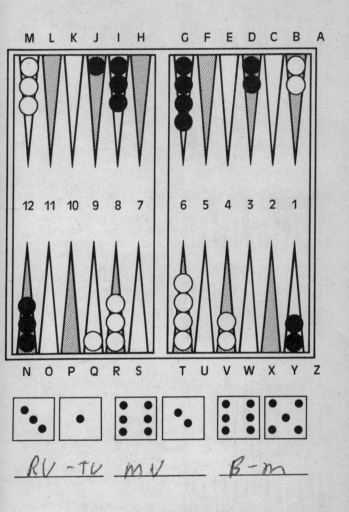

RV -TV   MV   B-M

3-1   M–Q=2
RU TU
The great opening roll of 3-1 is played here just as if it had been the first roll of the game. Covering your blot by moving M–Q is not necessary for that man is in little danger. (See page 271 in the Appendix for Suggested Ways to Play the Opening Rolls.)

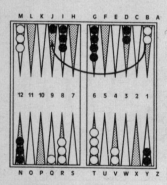

6-2   MS QS=3
B–J'
You should hit to stop your opponent from making his key points early. By doing so, you escape with a back man and put a third man of his back. This play will give you a good lead early in the game.

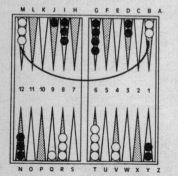

6-5   QW RW=3
      BH QV=1

B–M
Running a back man all the way to safety with an opening 6-5 roll is called "lover's leap"; it is a good play here. The builders in your outer board are more valuable if they are saved for making your 5-point or 7-point instead of your 3-point.

3

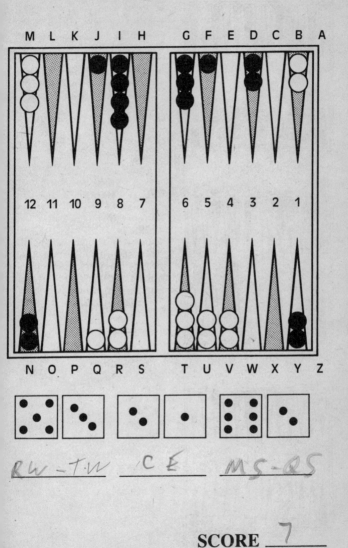

RW - T.W   C E   M S - Q S

SCORE 7

23

3

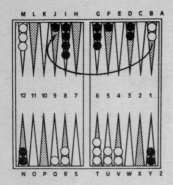

5-3
RW TW=2
MP QV=1

B–J'

By hitting, you also escape with a back man and slow your opponent's progress in making his inner board. This is sounder strategy than the alternative of making a fourth point in your own inner board.

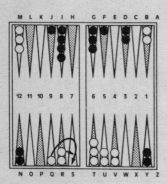

2-1
MO QR=2
BC MO=1
MO TU=1

QS RS

By all means make the 7-point. This will give you a strong block and the blot you leave on the 8-point can still be converted into another point if you subsequently throw a 5.

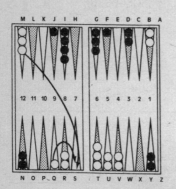

6-2
B–J'=3

MS QS

Making your 7-point will give you a five-point block and this is too good to pass up.

4

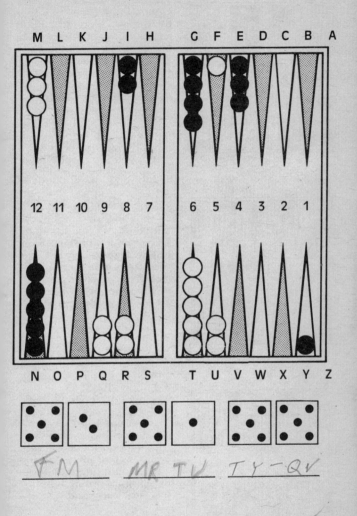

FM   MR TV TY – Qv

SCORE 15

25

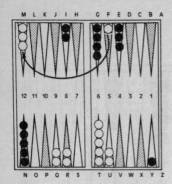

5-2 QV TV=3
F–M
By running to safety, your problems are over as far as getting your back men out. The alternative of making your 4-point has some merit, but this play will still leave a back man stranded in Black's inner board.

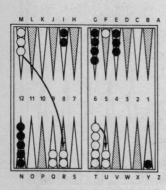

5-1 FK TU=2
TY' TU=2
F–L=1

MR TU
This is only a fair roll, but it can be played productively by constructing more builders. In the early stages of the game, a 1 is often played by moving TU to get an extra builder in your inner board.

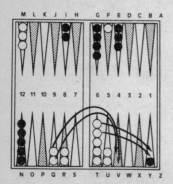

5-5 F–P QV2=3
QV2 RW2=2

QV2 TY2'
This type of double-5 play is a common occurrence when your opponent has left one back man behind. You get off to a good lead and often score a gammon by hitting and making a four-point inner board.

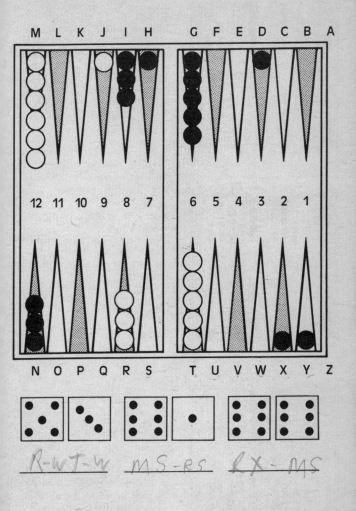

R-WT-W   MS-RS   RX-MS

SCORE 10

5

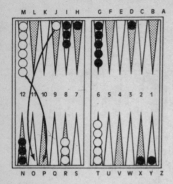

5-3 RW TW=3
MR MP=1

JO MP

Bringing two builders into your outer board will help you make your most important points. Do not worry about Black's split back men. He will have only 11 rolls with which to hit you and his inner board is too anemic to do you any harm.

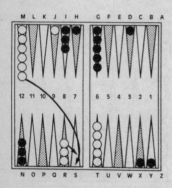

6-1 J–Q=2

MS RS

Your blot on Black's 9-point should be ignored; making your 7-point takes precedence here. Even if you are hit on the 9-point, you will have no trouble in entering.

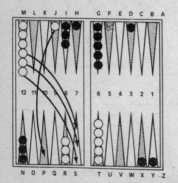

6-6 MS4=2
MS2 RX2'=2
RX2' M–Y'=1

JP MS3

You should not rush by moving too far into your inner board too early in the game. It is best to use the big double-6 roll to get a solid defense going — with extra builders in reserve for attacking blots or making points.

6

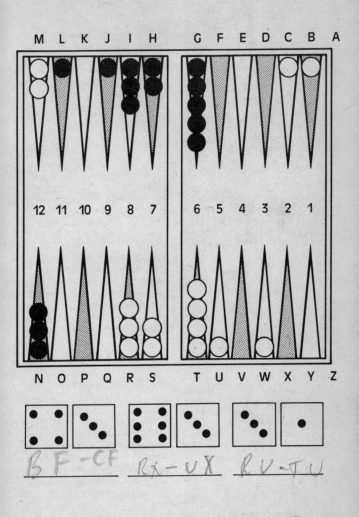

M L K J I H G F E D C B A

12 11 10 9 8 7 6 5 4 3 2 1

N O P Q R S T U V W X Y Z

BF - CF   RX - UX   RV - TU

SCORE 9

29

6

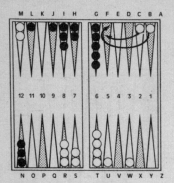

4-3
RU SW=3
C–J'=1

BF CF

By making your opponent's 5-point, you prevent him from making this point himself later and you keep your back men from being stranded deep in Black's inner board. In situations such as this, 4-3 is a very good roll.

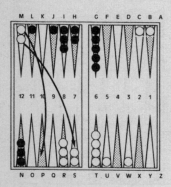

6-3
MS RU=4
B–K=3
RX RU=2
C–L'=1

MS MP

You should not hit Black on his 11-point because your inner board has two blots! Play to get your inner board strengthened so that if a shot materializes later, you will be ready with a good defense.

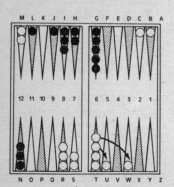

3-1
BC RU=2
RU TU=2

TW TU

What a fast way to make an inner board in a hurry! Making your opponent's 2-point as an alternative serves no useful purpose because you still will be trapped in his inner board.

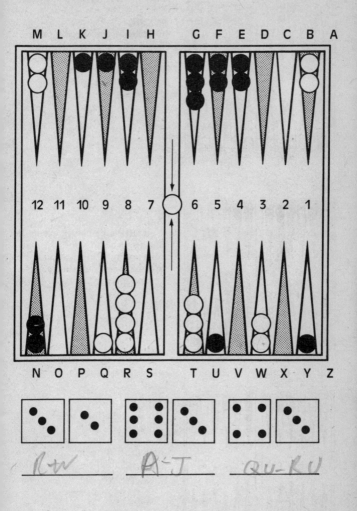

RW   R-J   QU-RU

SCORE 7½

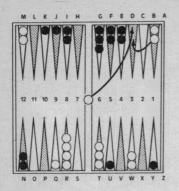

3-2   AC RU'=2
          AC QT=1

AD BD

Considering the circumstances, this is one of your best rolls. Making the 3-point will make it more difficult for Black to construct a strong blocking position.

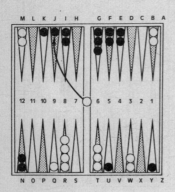

6-3   AD QW=1
          AD MS=1

A–J'

You have little choice except to enter and hit. If your opponent rolls poorly at his next turn, you may be able to turn the game around in your favor.

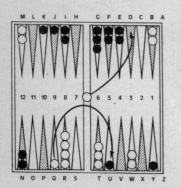

4-3   AD MQ=3

AD QU'

Because you have to leave a blot anyway, you might as well play aggressively and knock off your opponent. By doing so, you make it harder for him to make your valuable 5-point.

8

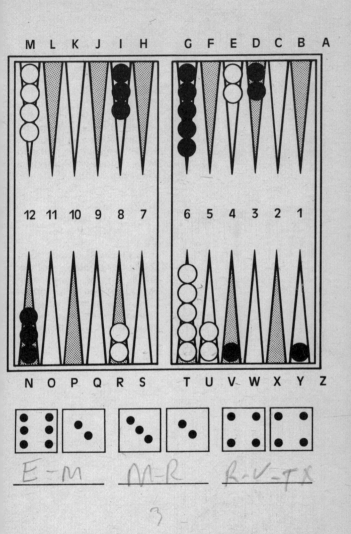

M L K J I H G F E D C B A

12 11 10 9 8 7 6 5 4 3 2 1

N O P Q R S T U V W X Y Z

E-M   M-R   R-V-TX

3

SCORE 11—

33

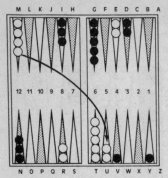

6-2   E–M=3
         MS TV'=2

M–U

Bringing a builder to your 5-point is a stronger play than running a back man to safety. It is better to hold your opponent's 4-point or 5-point early in the game for by doing so you make it difficult for him to bring down builders to his outer board. By adding another man to your 5-point, you give yourself extra ammunition to attack Black in your inner board.

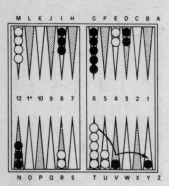

3-2   M–R=3
         MP MO=2
         MP TV'=1

TV'Y'

In this type of situation, you should hit two blots. You hope that by the time your opponent enters both men, you will have made extra points in your inner board and be far ahead positionally early in the game.

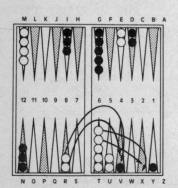

4-4   MQ2 RV2'=4
         MQ2 TX2=2
         RV2' UY2'=1

RV2' TX2

You are able to hit your opponent and make a fine four-point inner board besides. You could not ask for more.

BASIC QUIZZES

II
HITTING PLAYS

SCORE FOR THIS SECTION _63 ½_

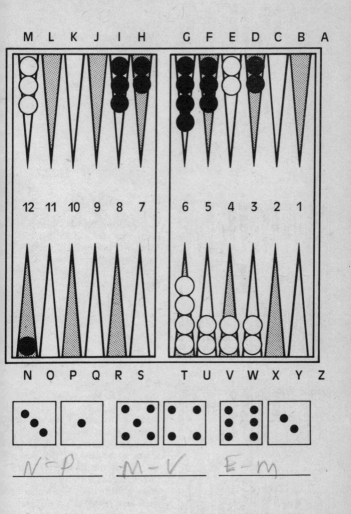

N-P   M-V   E-M

SCORE 3½

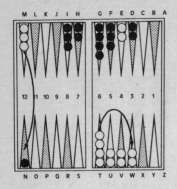

3-1   MN'Q=2
         MN' MP=2

MN' TW

The 3 is best played by moving from T so that you give yourself an extra builder. Now if Black enters, you will be in a better position to rehit him.

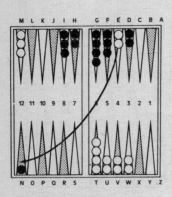

5-4   MR TX=1

E-N'

You must hit now because it is likely that you will not get another opportunity to do so. Your 4-point inner board is impressive and you are now the favorite to win the game.

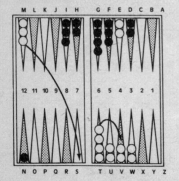

6-2   M-U=3
         E-M=1

MS TV

Because you cannot hit, it is best to strengthen your already adequate defense. Playing as shown is the best way to accomplish this as it gives you three builders with which to make a fifth point. Running a back man (E-M) is a weak play: Your remaining back man can be crushed, and it is better to play defensively as you are behind in the race.

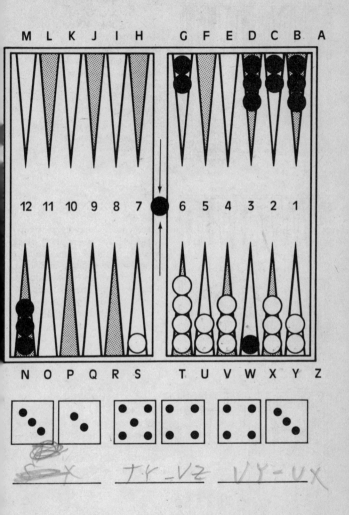

SCORE _____

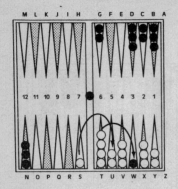

3-2
TW'Y=3
SV XZ=2
TW' VX=1

SU TW'
Because your opponent's inner board is only fair with little chance of being improved, you can take greater liberties in leaving a blot. If Black misses, you have three builders ready to cover.

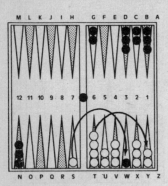

5-4
SX VZ=3
SX TX=1

SW' TY
Here you can play aggressively and shoot for gammon. If Black misses, you have a good chance at making an inside prime. If you are hit, barring very bad luck, you should be able to enter and come around before your opponent gets back on his feet.

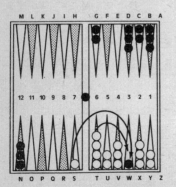

4-3
SW'Z=3
SVZ=1

SW' TW
By closing out Black, you give yourself the maximum chance to score a gammon.

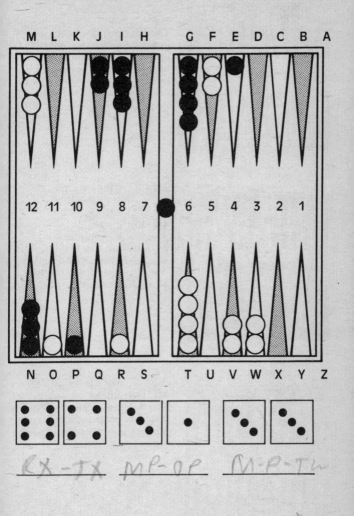

RX-TX   MP-OP   M-P-TW

SCORE 1 1/2

11

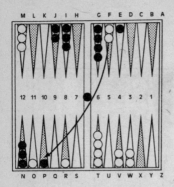

6-4 MQ OU=2
RX TX=1

F–P'
This easy play often goes unseen even by good players. By hitting, you place a second man on the bar and you have plenty of builders for making your 5-point or rehitting when Black enters.

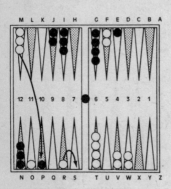

3-1 OP'S=4
MP'Q=3
RU TU=3

MP' RS
This is a fine roll with many good options. The best one, MP' RS, leaves you an extra builder which is invaluable in this type of shutout position.

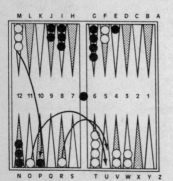

3-3 MP'S2=2

MP' O–U RU
This is a great roll and you cannot do any better than hit a second blot and also make your 5-point.

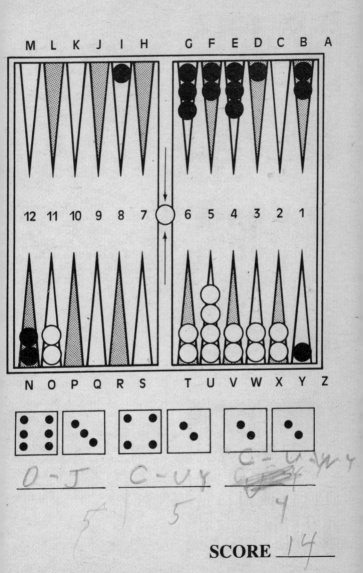

O – J   C – U 4   C – U 4

5 / 5   5   4

SCORE 14

12

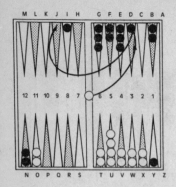

6-3   AD' OU=2

AD'J

It is better to hit and get out "while the going is good" on this one. If you hit and stay, Black may enter, put you on the bar and later cover. Going for the gammon is not quite worth the risk here.

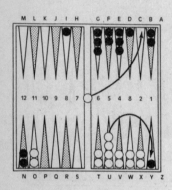

4-2   AC OS=1

AC UY'

It is not so much that you want to hit, it is that you have little choice. If you do the alternative play, you will leave your opponent a direct shot to hit you on the 7-point.

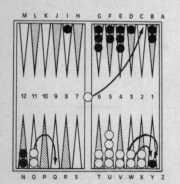

2-2   AC U–Y' UW=3
AC OQ2 UW=2
AC O–U=1

AC OQ WY2'

By exchanging your 3-point for your 1-point, you put Black on the bar and give yourself a good chance to hit another of his blots. This is a sound, aggressive play.

13

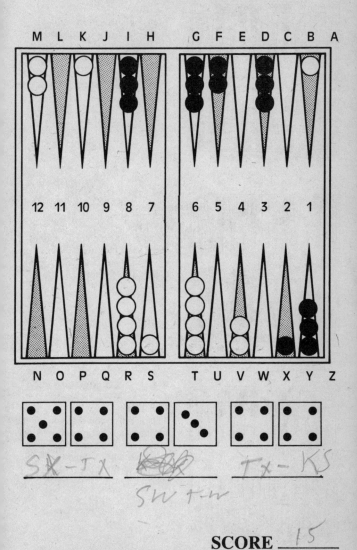

SCORE ___15___

45

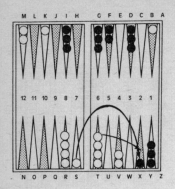

5-4   RW SW=2
SX' TX
Your 3-point is more valuable than your 2-point, but the difference here is that you can put Black on the bar. By doing so, you keep him from making a second point in your inner board.

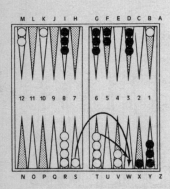

4-3   KN TX'=2
          KO SV=1
          SU TX'=1
SW TW
Because you obviously cannot leave your blot on the 7-point exposed, your best choice is to make the 3-point.

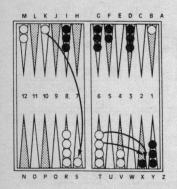

4-4   K–S MQ2=4
          MQ2 TX2'=2
K–S TX2'
This is a fine roll and you should not overlook hitting and making both the 2-point and the 7-point. Alternatively, making the 9-point instead of the 2-point also has merit.

14

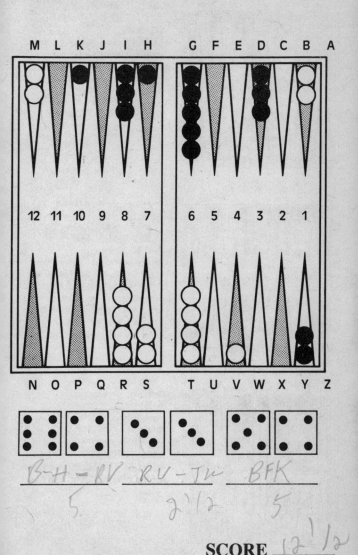

B-H - RV   RV - TU   BFK
        5.   2½2   5

SCORE 12½2

14

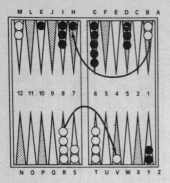

6-4 MS RV=2
BH'L=1

BH' RV
This is a good roll and you should use it to hit your opponent and cover your own blot on the 4-point. On your next turn, you will be in a good position to either make Black's 7-point or hit his other blot.

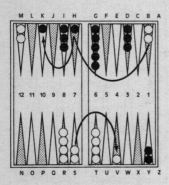

3-3 B–H' RU2=4
B–H2'=2
RU2 SV2=1
M–V MP=1

B–H'K' SV
This is a dream roll and you should take full advantage of it. After you hit the two blots, your opponent will be busy trying to bring them in and during this time you will be able to get a good inner-board defense built up.

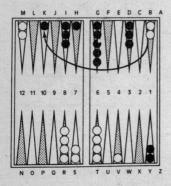

5-4 M–V=3
B–K'
By hitting, you also bring a back man out. You must try something aggressive, otherwise your opponent has a strong attacking position with many good rolls at his next turn.

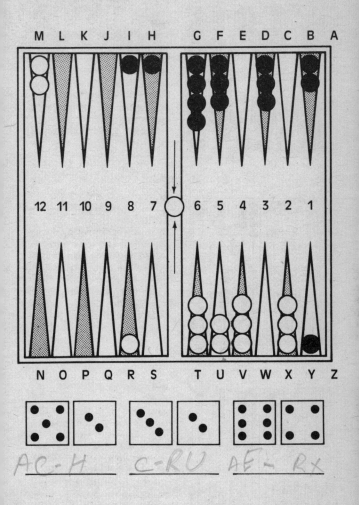

AC-H   C-RU   AE-RX

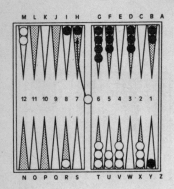

5-2   AC TY'=2
AC MR=1

A–H'

The best course of action is to enter and continue with the same man to the 7-point, hitting your opponent. Playing AC TY' is not nearly so effective, for you leave yourself on Black's 2-point and the man you employ to hit on your own 1-point is vulnerable to being hit back.

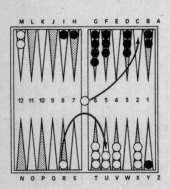

3-2   AC VY'=2
AC MP=2

AC RU

Because your opponent's inner board is as strong as yours, you should not hit on your 1-point and leave a blot. Playing RU for the 3 gets you an extra builder which will make it easier to make a fifth point in your home quadrant.

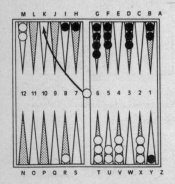

6-4   AE RX=1
A–K

You have to run for your life here! If you stay on the 4-point in an attempt to hit a blot, Black may easily point on you. By bringing your entered man out to K, you give yourself extra chances to hit Black if he decides to try to escape from your inner board.

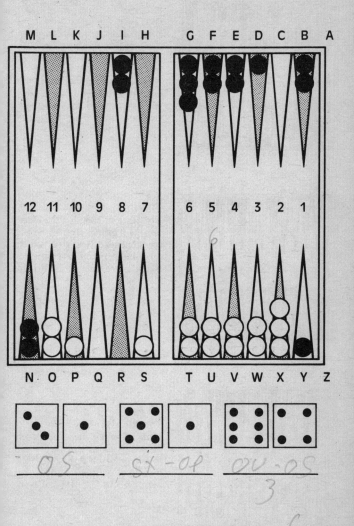

SCORE _____ 6

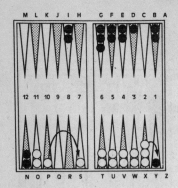

3-1   O–S=3
PS XY'
Of course you make a prime
and, as long as you have one,
you can take the liberty of
hitting on the 1-point! If Black
hits you back, you will get a
chance at hitting the blot in his
inner board. If you do so, you
will have a good chance to win a
gammon.

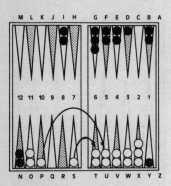

5-1   S–Y'=2
PU ST
You have to abandon the idea of
making a prime. By playing as
recommended, you give yourself
three builders to challenge
Black's lone man on the 1-point.

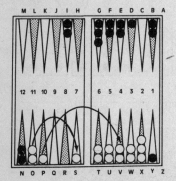

6-4   OU OS=3
             PT SY'=1
OS PV
The 4 is easy: You make a
prime. The 6 is more effectively
played by moving to your 4-point
to give yourself three rolls
instead of only two to make a
closed board (3-1, 1-3 and 1-1).

BASIC QUIZZES

III
THE MIDDLE GAME

SCORE FOR THIS SECTION _77_

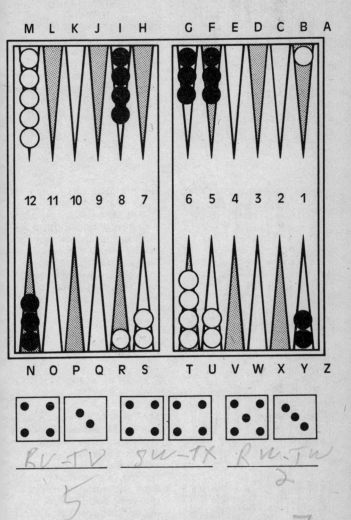

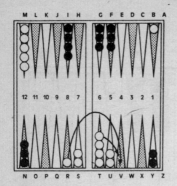

4-2   M–S=2
BD MQ=2
MQ MO=1

RV TV

Making the 4-point gives you four points in a row and the opportunity to bring down builders from the mid-point later with little risk of being hit. This is a powerful roll for you.

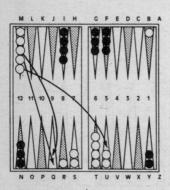

4-4   MQ2 TX2=3
M–U TX2=2

M–U MQ2

Your 2-point can wait; there is little sense in advancing too far forward when it is not necessary. The suggested play of bringing down builders will give you many good rolls at your next turn.

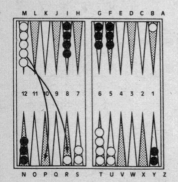

5-3   BE MR=3
RW TW=2

MR MP

The 5 must be played to make your 8-point and give you a very strong block. The 3 is more difficult, but bringing down another builder is a sound idea as it can only be hit with a 6-3 throw. If, instead, you move your back man three spaces, it can be hit and pointed on with nine rolls – a 25 percent chance for Black.

18

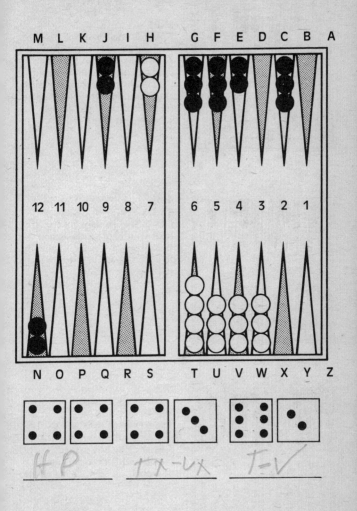

HP   TX-UX   T-V

SCORE 14

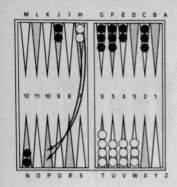

4-4   HL2 TX2=2
            TX4=1

H–P2

Run, run, run. You will be ahead in the race and will avoid all complications. Advancing only to L and making a 5-point board does not accomplish much at all, and, in fact, you would be forced to leave a blot if you subsequently threw 6-2 or 6-1.

4-3   UY VY=3

TX UX

Obviously you dare not break from your opponent's 7-point. Because your 2-point is superior to your 1-point, you should make it.

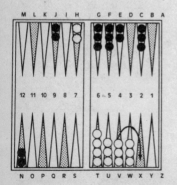

6-2   TV — =4
            WY — =2

VX —

The 6 is unplayable and the 2 is best handled by slotting on your 2-point as you have three builders with which to convert it to a point.

19

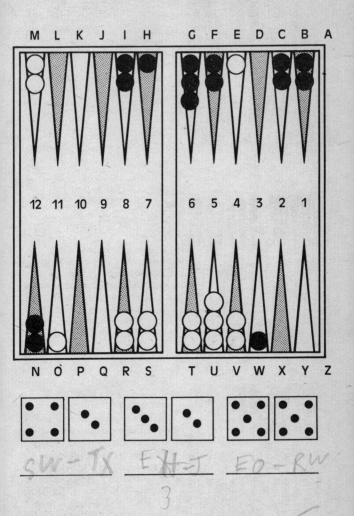

SW→TX   EH→I   ED→RW

3

SCORE 5

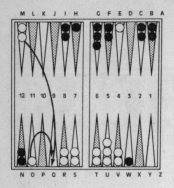

4-2

OS UW'=3
MQ UW'=1

MQ OQ

The prime – six points in a row – is the ultimate blocking position from which it is impossible for your opponent to escape. It is so strong here that you need not worry about blots that you leave on Black's 12-point and 4-point.

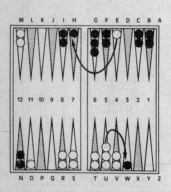

3-2

EH'J=3
EH' OQ=2
O–T=1
OR UW'=1

EH' UW'

Whenever you have the opportunity to hit two blots, you should generally do so. It is much harder for your opponent to enter two men from the bar instead of only one man. (See page 275 in the Appendix for Probabilities on Entering from the Bar.)

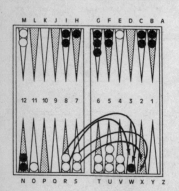

5-5

M–W2'=4
E–O RW2'=2

RW2' SX2

Making a prime by hitting with your two men from the mid-point is a strong play, but this nets you only a four-point inner board. A slightly better play is to hit and make a five-point board, passing up the prime. By doing so, Black will doubtless take longer to enter and you will have a greater chance then to pick up his other blot.

20

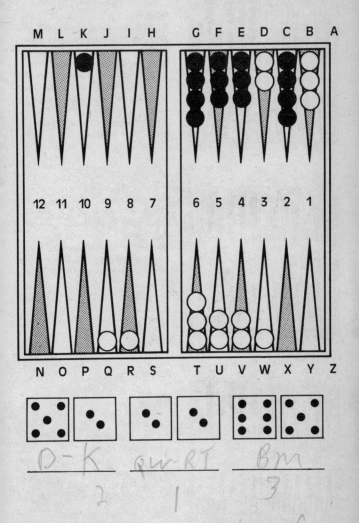

SCORE 6

61

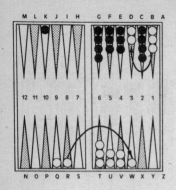

5-2

D–K'=2
B–I=1

BD RW

You have a good back-game position because you hold your opponent's 1-point and 3-point. You should not hit yet as your inner board is not ready. The better play is to make your 4-point and move a back man up so you will have a man with which to escape in case you throw high numbers.

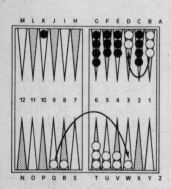

2-2

Q–W TV=2

BD Q–W

The double-2 roll here is played exactly the same as a 6-2 throw. Advancing a back man is mandatory so that you can keep your back game intact by having an extra man with which to run.

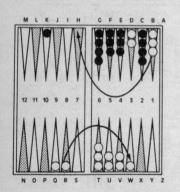

6-5

B–M=3
BH QV=2

BH RW

Your fifth man back is your "escape man"; you are able to run out with it and yet keep a strong back-game position intact. You need not care if you are hit on the 7-point, for you want to slow down to maintain the back-game position for as long as possible.

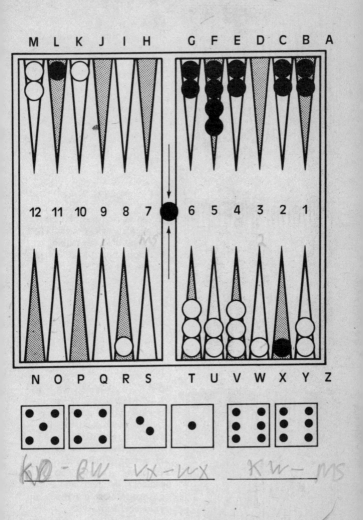

SCORE _____ 15

21

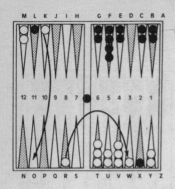

5-4 MQ RW=3
RW TX'=2

KO RW
If you hit Black's blot on the
2-point, you will leave a blot
yourself; your opponent's inner
board is too strong to warrant
this risk.

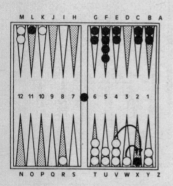

2-1 KM VW=2
VX' WX
If you missed this play, it was
through sheer oversight. Hitting
a second blot and making a
five-point board is an unbeatable
one-two punch.

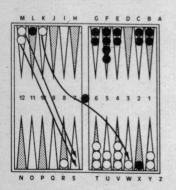

6-6 K–W MS RX'=1
K–W MS2
Because your opponent has a
five-point inner board, you
cannot go hog-wild hitting blots
when you are forced to leave
blots yourself. By playing as
indicated, you give yourself four
builders, in effect, and a fair
chance to close out Black on
your next turn.

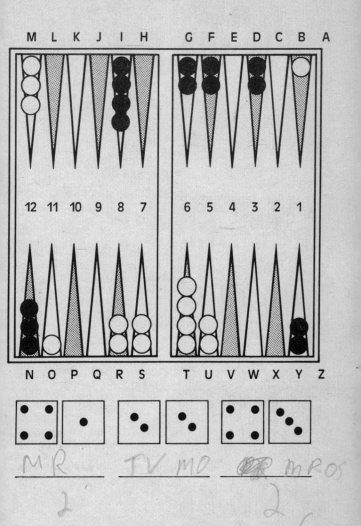

MR ___ TV MO ___ MROS

2   2   6

SCORE ___ 6

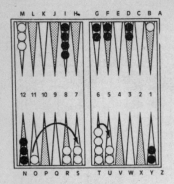

4-1   BC OS=2
M–R=2
MQ OP=1

OS TU

This a good roll and can be used to make three consecutive builders which will aid in making more points in your inner board. The alternative of moving a back man one space will not help in getting him out – and he could be pointed on if Black throws double 6 or double 3.

2-2   M–Q TV2=4
M–Q2=1

O–S TV2

There is no reason not to make your 4-point. The rest of the roll is close to a toss-up, but moving to your 7-point is less risky and you maintain an extra man on the mid-point which you will be at liberty to bring down later.

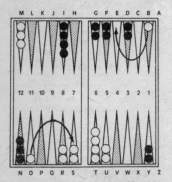

4-3   BE MQ=3
MQ OR=3
MP OS=2

BE OS

As long as Black, in effect, has only one builder bearing on his inner board, this might be a good time to move your back man into position to vacate.

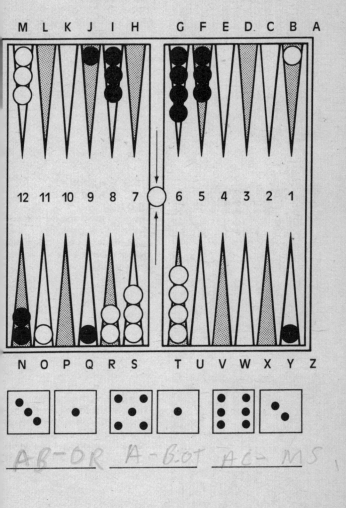

AB-DR   A-B.OT   AC-MS

SCORE 11

23

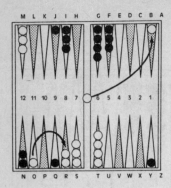

3-1   AD OP=1
          A–E=1

AB OR

Black has a good position and you are behind in the game. A sound, conservative play is the only sane course of action.

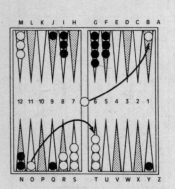

5-1   AB MR=2
          AB TY'=1

AB OT

The 1 is forced and the 5 is best played by not gambling. You are much the worse for the situation and should not leave a blot for Black to hit.

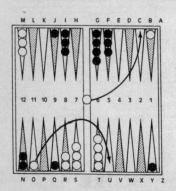

6-2   AC SY'=2
          AC MS=1

AC OU

The 2 is forced and the 6 is best handled by slotting your 5-point. If you must leave a blot, leave it where it will do the most good.

24

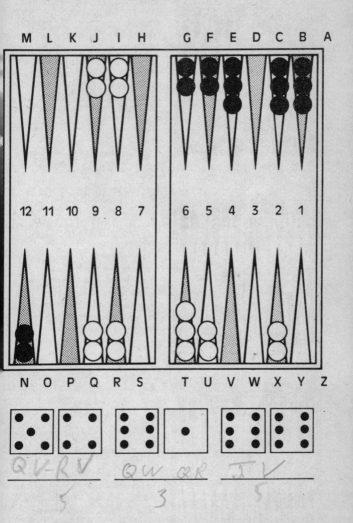

QV-RV
5

QW QR
3

JV
5

SCORE 13

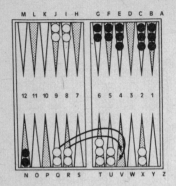

5-4

QU TY=2
RW RV=1

QV RV

It may appear awkward to leave two blots in your outer board, but making a fourth inner point takes precedence over aesthetics. You will now be in good shape in the likely event that Black will soon leave you a shot.

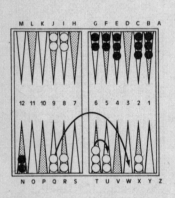

6-1

QW RS=4
QW QR=3
R–Y=1
IO IJ=1

QW TU

Do whatever you can to get your inner board ready for the shot from Black that is bound to materialize. If you break from I, you give yourself less chance to hit your opponent when he is forced to flee from the 12-point.

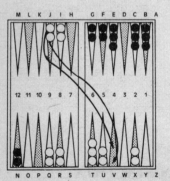

6-6

JP2 QW2=3
QW2 RX2=3
IO2 JP2=1

J–V2

In spite of throwing double 6, you are way behind in the running game. Thus, you must not run with the four men in the opponent's outer board; if you do so, you will lose the race. Stay back. If Black throws a single 6, you will have a shot at him.

BASIC QUIZZES

IV
END-GAME PLAYS

SCORE FOR THIS SECTION _____

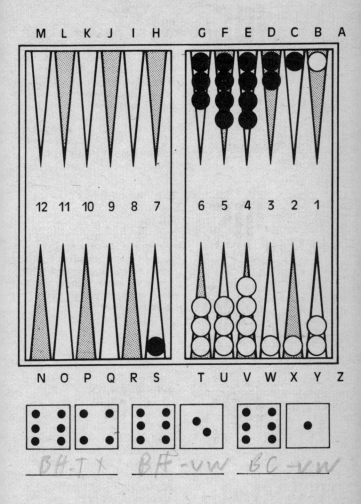

BH.JX   BF-VW   GC-VW

SCORE VI

25

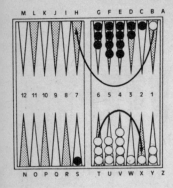

6-4   BH UY=2
         B–L=1

BH TX

The 6 is forced and the 4 should be played in your inner board so that you can keep your lone man as far away as possible from Black. By staying on his 7-point, he can hit you with only two throws (6-5); if you move to L, he can hit you with six throws (6-1, 5-2, 4-3). (See page 275 in the Appendix for the table on Probabilities of Hitting a Blot.)

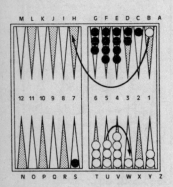

6-2   BH VX=5
         B–J=1

BH UW

You will leave your opponent fewer shots if you stay 11 points away from him instead of only nine points away. The general guideline here is do not come closer to your opponent when you are seven or more pips away.

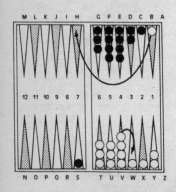

6-1   BH WX=4
         BHI=2
         BC'I=1

BH VW

You should not dream of hitting your opponent as your inner board is not ready. Run out to the 7-point and stay there, leaving the fewest number of shots for Black to hit you.

74

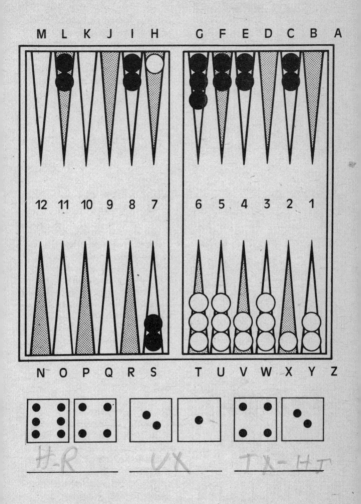

M L K J I H G F E D C B A

12 11 10 9 8 7 6 5 4 3 2 1

N O P Q R S T U V W X Y Z

H-R VX TX-HJ

SCORE 9

26

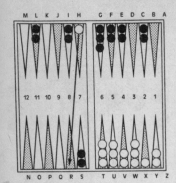

6-4   HN TX=1

H–R

The 6 is forced and the 4 should be played to move as close as possible to Black on the 7-point. By doing so, you will leave him only 11 ways to hit you instead of 15 ways. Come as close as you can to your opponent when you are six or fewer pips away.

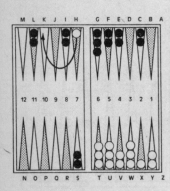

2-1   HJ WX=4
      U–X=1

H–K

If you stay where you are on Black's 7-point, you leave a double direct shot. By playing your 2 to pass his 8-point, you leave only a single direct shot. The 1 is a tougher choice as you leave an equal number of shots whether you occupy J or K. By moving to K, though, you do get that much closer to home.

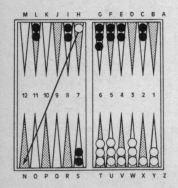

4-2   HJ TX=3

H–N

By moving all the way to your 12-point, you leave the fewest shots (15); if you go only as far as J, Black can hit you with a 2 (12 ways) or a 9 (5 more ways). Furthermore, by moving all the way, you get yourself that much closer to your inner board.

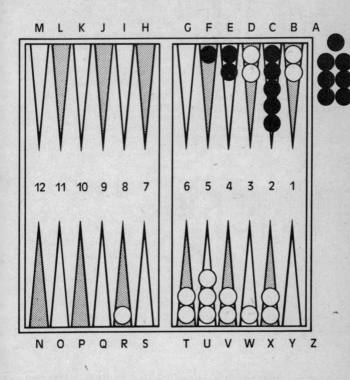

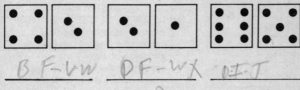

B F - V W   D F - W X   D E - J

                       2   1

SCORE 8

27

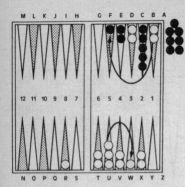

4-2 DF' RV=1
DF'J=1
UY WY=1

BF' UW

You have a choice of hitting with a 2 or 4, but the decision is easy: The 2 must be used to make your five-point board. All the other alternative plays are weak.

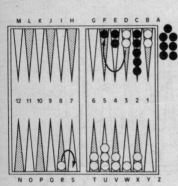

2-1 DF' UV=4
DF' WX=2

DF' RS

By all means hit, but leave your 3-point slotted. Even if this man is hit, your opponent has no inner board and you will enter easily. You should try at all costs to make a five-point board. By playing your 1 from R to S you have an extra man to bear down on your 1-point should Black enter there.

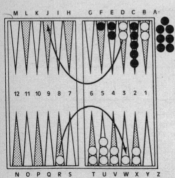

6-5 DJ DI=2
BH RW=1

DJ RW

Even though breaking your opponent's 3-point is indicated, you will still have a strong back-game position. Use the 5 to add to your powerful inner board.

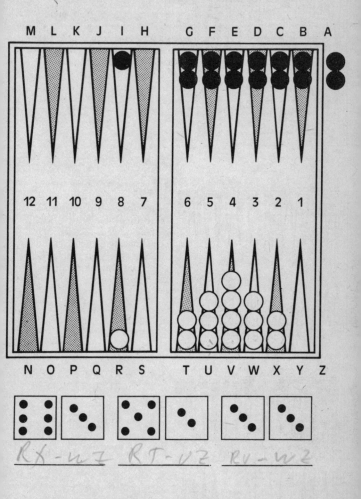

RX - UZ   RT - UZ   RV - UZ

SCORE 12

28

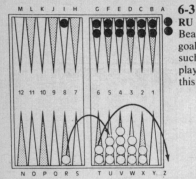

6-3   RX WZ=2
RU TZ
Bearing men off the 6-point is a goal whenever you have a choice such as this. The bear-in/bear-off play is much more efficient when this high point is cleared.

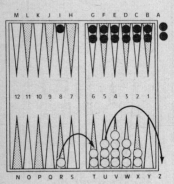

5-2   RW XZ=3
RT UZ
Bear-in/bear-off plays such as these are generally best managed by playing your dice as economically as you can.
Bearing in to your 6-point is not so helpful, but taking a man off the 5-point instead of the 2-point offsets this factor.

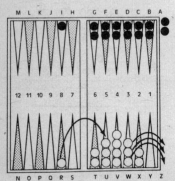

3-3   RU VY WZ2=3
       RU T–Z TW=1
RU WZ3
There are many good choices here, but taking off three men to give yourself only 12 men left is too good to refuse.

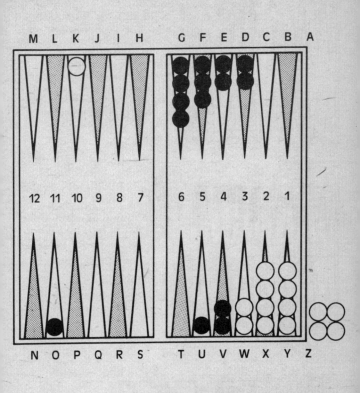

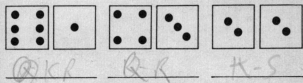

SCORE _12_

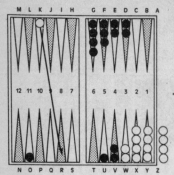

6-1   KQ XY=2
K–R
If you are six or fewer points away from your opponent, you should move as close as possible to him. This axiom is just as true when your opponent has men on two adjacent points. By playing 6-1 to move an extra pip closer, you give Black two fewer shots to hit you (24 throws instead of 26).

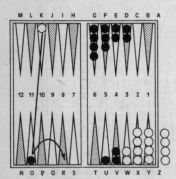

4-3   KNR=1
KO'R
By hitting, you give Black fewer return shots as he must use one of his dice to enter from the bar.

2-2   K–O'–S=2
K–O' WY2
This is one of the rare times when you intentionally break up your inner board! The reason here is to keep your lone blot outside the direct range of Black's men on your 4-point; thus, you leave him fewer return shots to hit you.

30

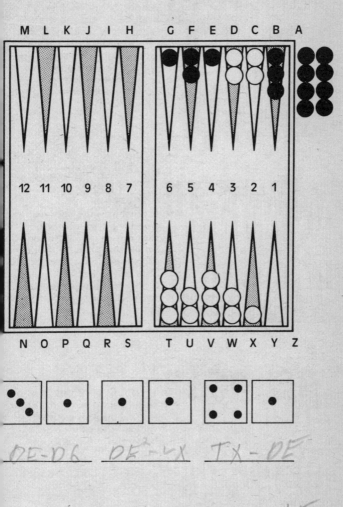

OE-DG   DE²-LX   TX-OE

SCORE __15__

83

30

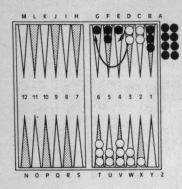

3-1   T–X=1
DG' DE'
Your opponent just threw a
nightmare 6-3 roll and was
forced to give a quadruple shot.
Even though your blot is left
uncovered on the 2-point, you
have to rise to the occasion and
hit both blots. By doing so, you
have an excellent chance to win
the game.

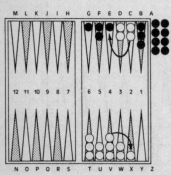

1-1   DE' TU V–X=5
           DE2' V–X=2
C–E' V–X
If you missed this one, you
probably played too hastily. You
must play so as to leave yourself
a triple shot to hit the other blot
on your next turn; there are two
plays that accomplish this and
either one is acceptable. Black
has no defense so you can go all
out.

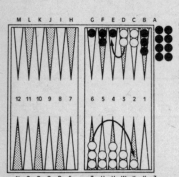

4-1   CG' DE'=2
DE' TX
There is no immediate need to
hit both blots; make your board
first and the odds are well in
your favor to hit the other blot
before Black recovers.

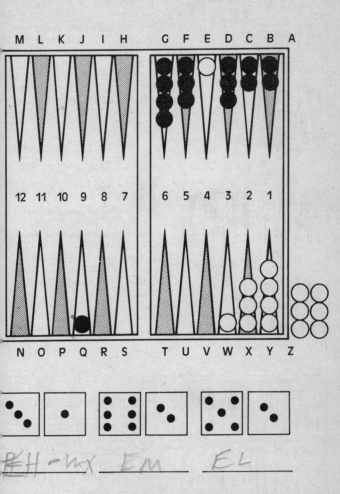

EH -w.x EM EL

SCORE 11

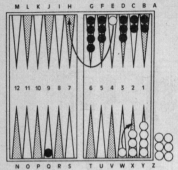

3-1   EH XY=4
            E–I=2

EH WX

The 3 is forced and places you
nine pips away from being hit.
Your opponent can hit you with
five rolls (6-3, 5-4, 3-3); if you
move the same man the 1, you
will be eight pips away and there
will be six ways instead of five
to hit you (6-2, 5-3, 4-4, 2-2).

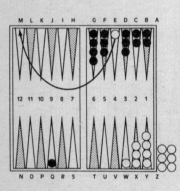

6-2   EK WY=2

E–M

The 6 is forced and places you
six pips away from being hit.
Your opponent could hit you
with 17 rolls out of the 36
possible ones. If, however, you
move the same man two more
spaces, you can be hit in only 15
ways.

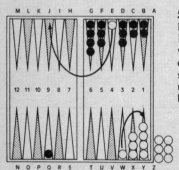

5-2   E–L=1

EJ WY

If you run your last man all the
way, you will be in direct range
of being hit by 15 rolls; if you
stay seven pips away, you are
not in direct range and you can
be hit by only six rolls.

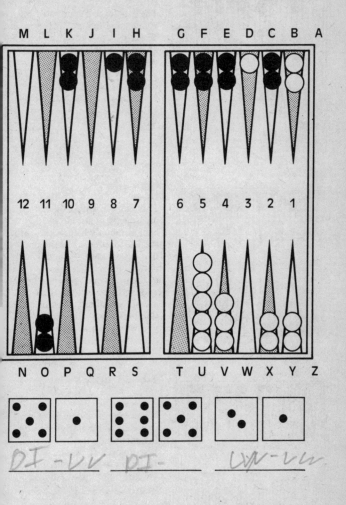

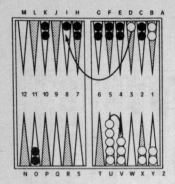

5-1   DI'J=3

DI' UV

The 5 is forced: You must hit. By electing to stay on I, you will be six pips away from Black on O. If Black throws a 6, he will use it to enter from the bar; thus your blot is relatively safe. This concept is called duplication and is discussed in the Advanced Quizzes.

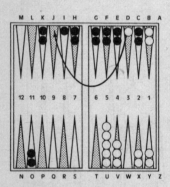

6-5

DJ —

This is more a quiz on rules than on strategy. The rule in backgammon which occurs with the least frequency is the one that states when a player can play either number but not both of them, he must play the higher one. In this problem, then, you are not permitted to hit the blot that is five pips away because you would not be able to play a 6.

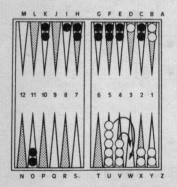

2-1   BD VW=2
       BD UV=2

UW VW

When you have control of your opponent's 1-point, you are in the game until the bitter end. Use this roll to make your 3-point; it will almost surely be the last inner-board point you get to make this game.

BASIC QUIZZES

V
BEARING OFF

SCORE FOR THIS SECTION _____ 90.1/2

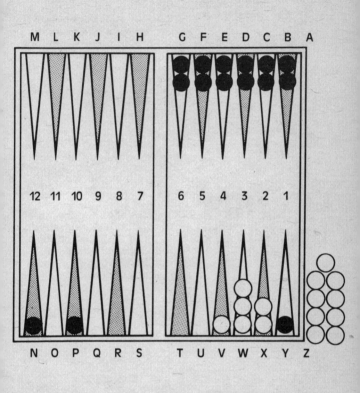

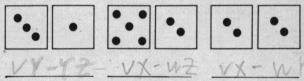

VY-YZ - VX-WZ VX-WY

SCORE _15_

33

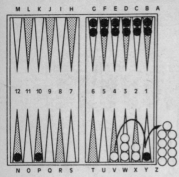

3-1   VWZ=1
VY'Z

You must hit in this situation: If your opponent then enters with a 4, 5 or 6, he passes you and you are assured a gammon. If, instead, you elect not to hit, he will stay on your 1-point and you will have to yield a blot on your next roll unless you luckily throw 2-1 or 1-1.

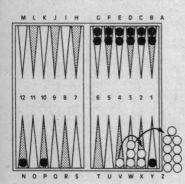

5-2
VX WZ

The rules of backgammon state that you can play your dice in any order as long as you play both of them. Thus, play the only way in which you do not have to leave a blot!

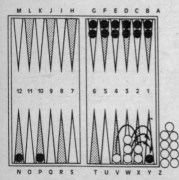

2-2   V–Z XZ2=2
VX WY'3

You could bear off three men, but by doing so you would leave three men bare on your 3-point – almost a sure shot next roll. It is best, instead, to bury your opponent and force him to enter past you.

34

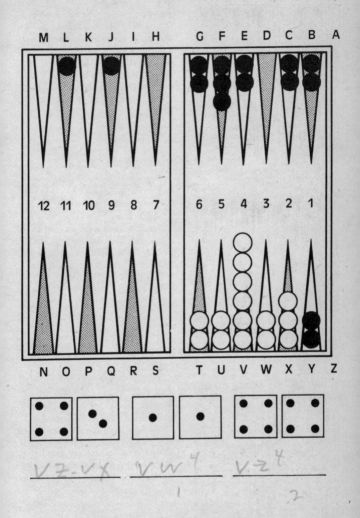

VZ-VX VW⁴ VZ⁴

1   2

SCORE 5

93

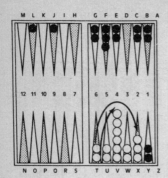

4-2 VZ XZ=2
TX TV
If you bear off two men, you will be in serious trouble if you roll 6-5 at the next turn: You will be forced to yield two blots! It is safer not to leave two men on each of the two highest points when there is a good alternative play.

1-1 V–X2=2
  VW4=1
TU2 VW2
Spreading your men as in the suggested play will make your next roll shot-free and will make bearing off much easier on the following rolls, too. Also, you avoid giving the double shot with a 6-5 throw.

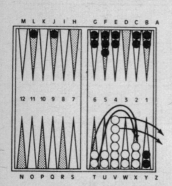

4-4 VZ4=2
TX2 VZ2
So that you do not leave yourself thin on the high points – and prone to a possible double shot – you should clear the 6-point. Only if you had a very good chance for a gammon would it be worth it to bear off four men.

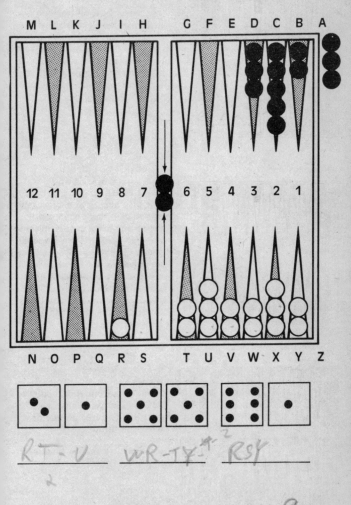

R T - V
_____
2

W R - T Y +2
_____

R S Y
_____

SCORE 9
_____

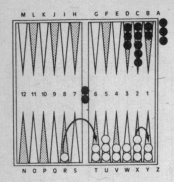

2-1   R–U=2
RT XY
The safest bear-off position is three men on the 6-point and three men on the 5-point. Not only will you not have to give a shot on your next roll, but whatever you throw, it will not leave you an awkward setup for the following roll.

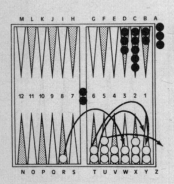

5-5   RW UZ3=2
RW TY2 UZ
The idea here is to play as safe as you can; there is no sense taking any extra chance because it is impossible to win a double game. (The rules state that when an opponent has borne off men, a player can no longer win a gammon or backgammon.) By playing as indicated, you leave fewer chances for giving a shot later on.

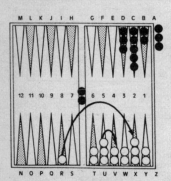

6-1   R–Y=2
RX UV
By moving from your 5-point to your 4-point, you make your next roll shot-free no matter what you throw.

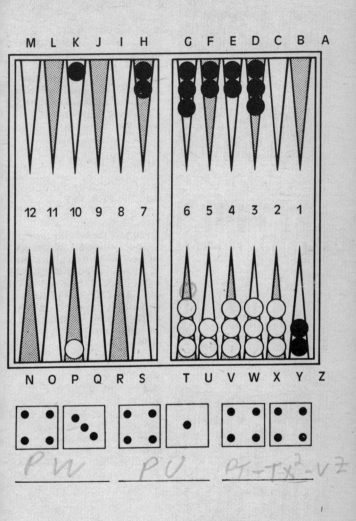

PW   PU   PT-TX²-VZ

SCORE 12

36

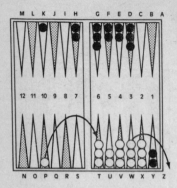

4-3   P–W=2
PT WZ
In bearing off, the idea is to
position yourself so you are least
likely to leave a shot on your
next roll. By having an even
number of men on your 6-point
as opposed to an odd number of
men, there are fewer rolls that
will put you in jeopardy at your
next turn.

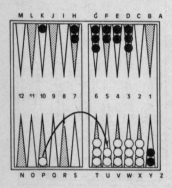

4-1   PT WX=3
          PT VW=2

P–U
If you play the 4 to the 6-point
and the 1 elsewhere within, you
do leave an even number of men
on the 6-point, but you will leave
a shot if you next throw 5-4. The
best rule of thumb in positioning
your men is to leave three men
on your 6-point and three men
on your 5-point (when your
opponent occupies your 1-point).

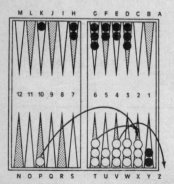

4-4   PT VZ3=2
P–X TX VZ
If you bear off three men, you
leave a cavity on an interior
point. You should always
beware of doing this, for it
makes it much more difficult to
bear off without leaving a shot
later.

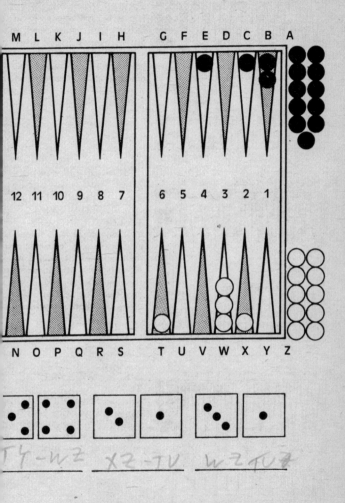

TY-WZ XZ-TV WZTVZ

SCORE 15

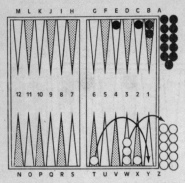

5-4 TX WZ=2
TY WZ

It may not make much differen[ce] in this case because Black will probably be off in two turns; still, the best policy here is to get the most pips out of your dice and also spread your men out.

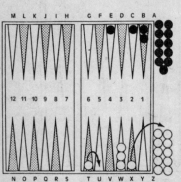

2-1 W–Z=3
TV WX=1
TU WY=1

TU XZ

You have to bear off a man so as to leave only four men and the chance of throwing a winn[ing] set of doubles at your last turn. By playing as suggested, you w[ill] be off at your next turn if you throw double 6 or double 5.

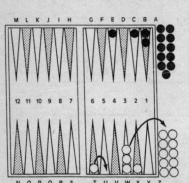

3-1 WZ XY=1
TU WZ

The 3 is easy and the 1 is best handled by clearing your 6-po[int]. Now double 5 or double 6 wil[l] get you off at your next — an[d] probably final — turn.

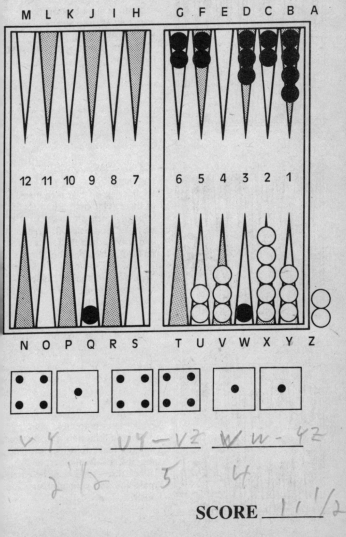

V Y   V Y — V Z   W W — 4 Z

2 ½   5   4

SCORE 11 ½

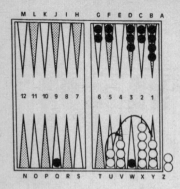

4-1   VZ YZ=2
UY UV

If you bear off two men, you are liable to leave a blot on your next roll. If, instead, you move within, there is no roll that will force you to give a shot on your next turn.

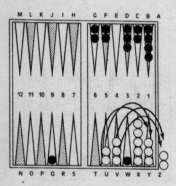

4-4   UY VZ3=3
UY2 VZ2

By bearing off two men instead of three, you can be hit only if your opponent throws a 1 (11 ways); if you bear off three men and leave a blot on U, you can be hit if your opponent throws a 2 (12 ways, as double 1 hits). With your opponent's inner board so strong, you must take the safer alternative.

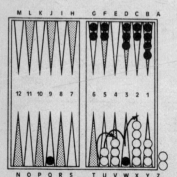

1-1   VW'3 YZ=4
         UV2 YZ2=2
         X–Z YZ2=1
U–W'X UV

The safest way to avoid leaving a shot later is to clear your 5-point and hit and run. By doing so, you leave four men on your 4-point, a safe number, and if Black throws a 5 or 6, he enters past you and your problems are over.

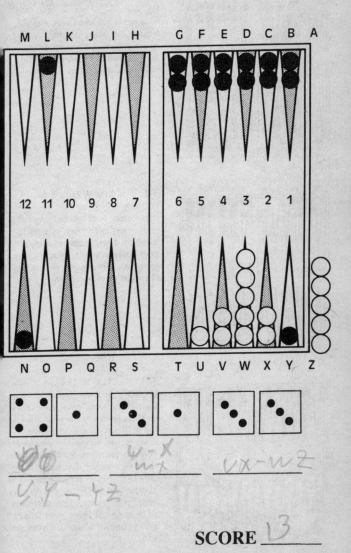

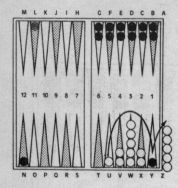

4-1   UVZ=1
UY'Z

You must hit and then bear off.
You place Black on the bar and
he may be forced to enter on
your 5-point or 6-point and thus
pass you altogether.

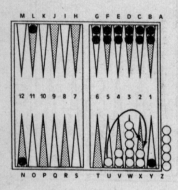

3-1   UV WZ=2
UX WX

It is better to forgo bearing off a
man in order to play safe and
leave an even number of men on
your highest point. Black has a
prime and so caution is surely
the right advice.

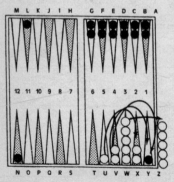

3-3   UX WZ3=3
UX VY2' WZ

By hitting, you leave yourself in
less danger on your next turn,
for if Black enters on a high
inner point, he passes you and
you are totally safe. In addition,
there is another dividend: If he
should fail to enter or you throw
another set of doubles, you may
score a gammon. The alternative
of bearing off three men leaves
you prone to a shot on your next
turn.

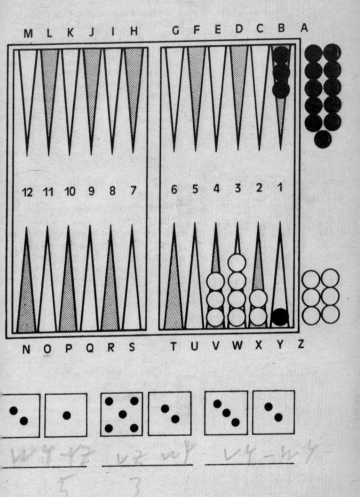

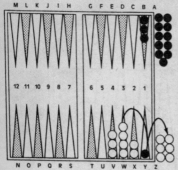

2-1   WXZ=2
WY'Z

This position resulted after Black bore off 12 men and then left a shot. White hit and bore off several men before Black entered on the 1-point. The 2-1 roll is handled best by hitting to place your opponent on the bar. Now Black needs 25 instead of 24 pips to get this man around and off.

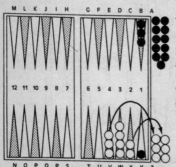

5-2   VZ WY'=3
VZ XZ

With either choice of play, you leave a blot that can be hit with a 1. Thus, you might as well bear off two men instead of only one man. The race to victory is going to be a close one!

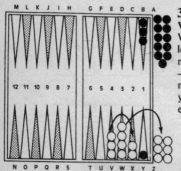

3-2   VY' WY=2
VX WZ

When you bear off a man, you leave yourself with only eight men and hopefully four rolls left — a fair chance to win. If you make your 1-point, the only way you can win is if Black does not enter and you roll well.

ADVANCED QUIZZES

VI
THE OPENING GAME

SCORE FOR THIS SECTION _70_

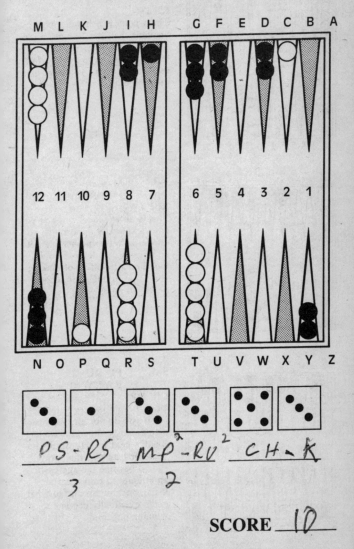

OS - RS

MP² - RV² CH - K

3

2

SCORE 10

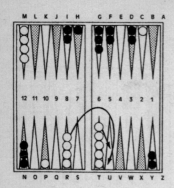

3-1   PS RS=3
M–Q=1

RU TU

The 5-point is generally more valuable than the 7-point and in this case it is particularly better because you get to move off of two points where you have many men piled up.

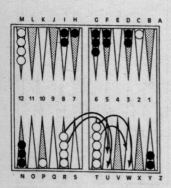

3-3   M–S2=3
MP2 RU2=2

RU2 TW2

This is an excellent roll and you have a splendid opportunity to unpile from two points and get an inner-board defense going, too. The alternative of making your 7-point does not accomplish nearly so much.

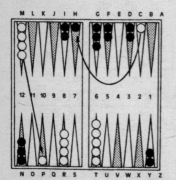

5-3   PU RU=2
RW TW=1

CH' MP

Your 5-point is very valuable, but if you do not hit, your back man could be fenced in on Black's next roll. In desperate situations such as this, you should become the aggressor in an attempt to turn a certain losing position around to what could eventually become a winning position.

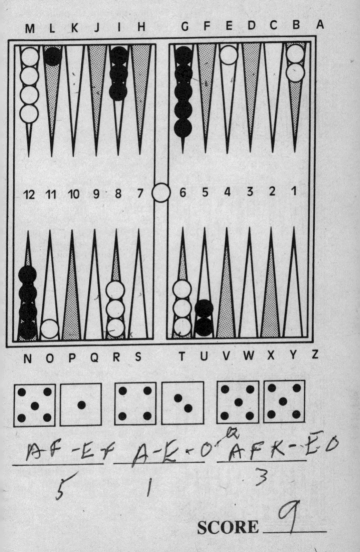

$$\frac{Af - Ef}{5} \quad \frac{A - E - O}{1} \quad \frac{AFK - EO}{3}$$

SCORE 9

42

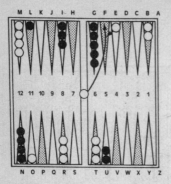

5-1 AB OT=2
AF EF
Your opponent's 5-point is a key spot to occupy at the beginning of the game: You keep him from making it and you obstruct him from leaving blots in his outer board for building points.

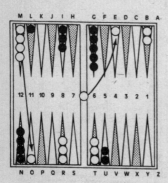

4-2 AE TV=2
AE RT=1
AE MO
Your opponent's 4-point is a good point to make even though it is not so effective as his 5-point. Your 11-point is valuable here, for it acts as a bar-point for your opponent's men on the 5-point.

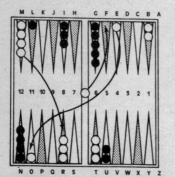

5-5 AF E–O RW=3
AF M–W RW=2
AF E–O MR
There is no hurry to make your 3-point; it is not wise to advance so far so early in the game. Moving a lone man from your opponent's 4-point ten pips to safety on your own 11-point is the best alternative.

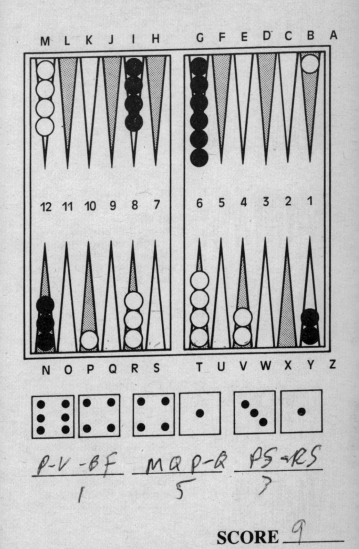

P-V -BF   MQP-Q   PS -RS
    1   5   3

SCORE 9

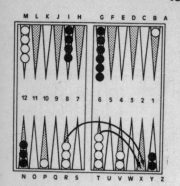

6-4 B–L=4
MQ PV=2

RX TX

Whenever your opponent has piled up because of poor throws, you should not be in a hurry to run. Stay back and wait for a shot which will invariably materialize. In the interim, get a good inner defense ready.

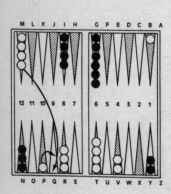

4-1 BF PQ=3
P–U=2

MQ PQ

There is little else you can do except to make your 9-point. This move will prohibit your opponent from splitting his back men if he throws a 2 or 4.

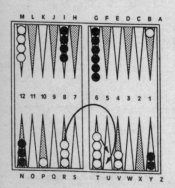

3-1 PS RS=3

RU TU

The classic opening 3-1 play is called for: The 5-point is generally more valuable than the 7-point. In this case, particularly, it is best to get a good inner board against your weak opponent. And if your outer man is hit, it will be no disadvantage to you.

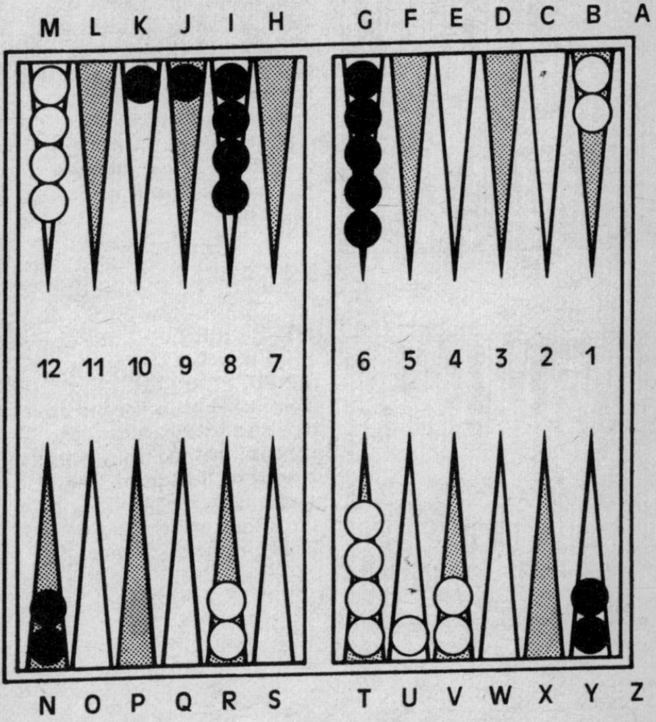

M L K J I H   G F E D C B A

12 11 10 9 8 7   6 5 4 3 2 1

N O P Q R S   T U V W X Y Z

BJ⁴   BE   T-V   JX-VY
  2   2   2

SCORE 6

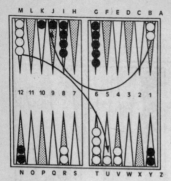

4-4   BF2 M–U=3
B–J' M–U

Your opponent's 5-point is valuable, but by hitting instead, you place Black on the bar and give yourself the top three points in your inner board. If your opponent should fail to enter, or if he enters with an awkward roll (such as 5-3), you will win a very fast game and perhaps a gammon.

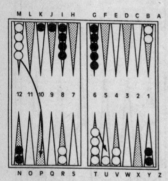

3-1   BE TU=2
        RU TU=1

MP TU

You should be inclined to defer moving a back man as your opponent has too many builders bearing on his 4-point. The simple tactical play of making the 5-point and bringing down a builder is the best option.

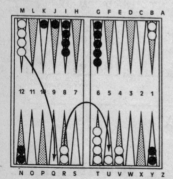

4-3   TX UX=2
        BF RU=1

MQ RU

Making your 5-point is better than making your 2-point and advancing men so far forward. The fact that you leave two outer blots should not detract you here.

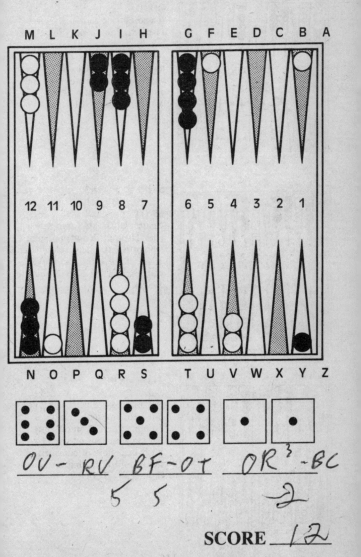

OV — RV BF — OT OR³ — BC
5 5   2

SCORE 12

6-3 F–O=2
OU RU
If you choose to make your
11-point, you do rid yourself of
two blots, but your defensive
position is helped only
minimally. In addition, you may
have difficulty in moving off this
outer point later on. The
optimum choice is to make your
5-point.

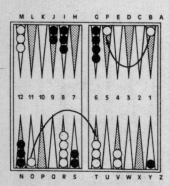

5-4 F–O=3
  BF MR=2
BF OT
Again you should forgo making
your 11-point. Your opponent's
5-point is extremely valuable and
in the process you can move
your blot on the 11-point out of
danger.

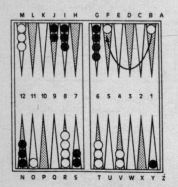

1-1 BC O–R=2
B–F
All four 1's are used to move
one man and make the vital
5-point. The risk in possibly
having your blot on the 11-point
hit is negligible in comparison to
the benefit of having the
opponent's 5-point.

46

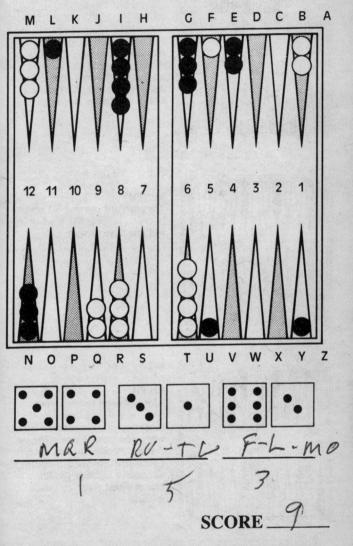

MAR RU-TU F-L-MO

1   5   3

SCORE 9

119

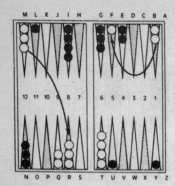

5-4
BF TY'=3
MQ TY'=2
F–O=1

BF MR

Playing the 4 to make your opponent's 5-point gives you a valuable anchor and this play should not be passed up. The play of the 5 is more difficult and the passive move of bringing a man down seems most logical.

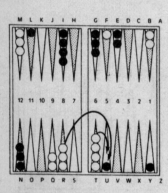

3-1
B–F=3
M–Q=1

RU' TU

The standard opening 3-1 play is in order; making Black's 5-point will just have to wait.

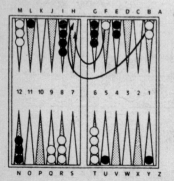

6-2
FL' MO=3
MS QS=2

BH FH

This is a good roll and your position will be nicely solidified in all four quadrants of the board when you make Black's 7-point. Another choice, making your own 7-point, is not a comparable alternative because you leave a blot in direct range on your 9-point.

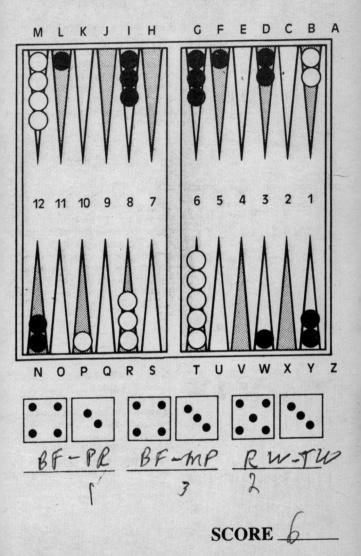

BF - PR   1

BF - MP   3

R W - TW   2

SCORE 6

47

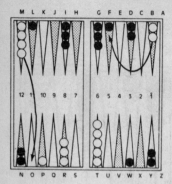

4-2 RV TV=2
BF' PR=1

BF' MO
Early in the game when your opponent slots his 5-point, you should invariably hit. You want to do all you can to stop him from making this key point. By hitting, you also move a back man forward and you make it easier to secure this point for yourself.

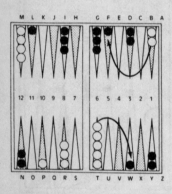

4-3 BF' MP=3
BF' PS=1

BF' TW'
Hit two blots! This is an aggressive move that often leads to a blitz: a situation at the beginning of the game in which your opponent never quite gets back on his feet and you go on to gammon him.

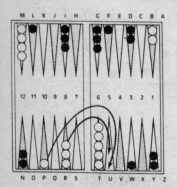

5-3 RW' TW=2
BE MR=1

PU RU
It appears to be a close choice, but your 5-point is a very powerful space to control. Alternatively, if you hit and make your 3-point, Black will enter with little trouble — and possibly make your 5-point or 4-point in the process.

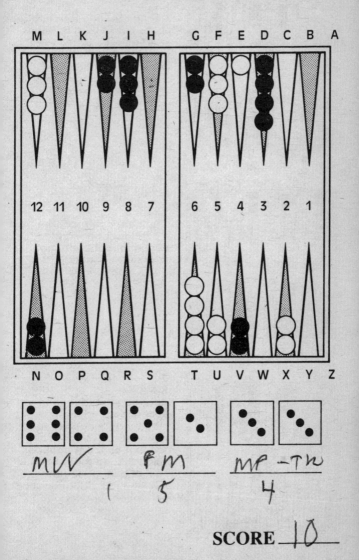

MN

FM   5

MP - TN   4

SCORE 10

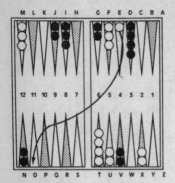

6-4   M–W=1
E–O

Many 6-4 and 6-3 simple running plays are overlooked by players at all levels of skill. By running, you get the lone man in your opponent's inner board to relative safety and on its way to your own inner board.

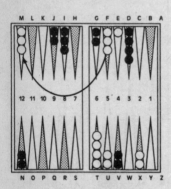

5-2   MO TY=1
         M–T=1

F–M

This is a safe play and since you are ahead in a running game, there is no need to take any other course of action.

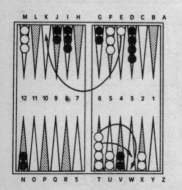

3-3   MP3 TW=4
E–K TW2

Bringing two or three men down from M is a possible alternative, but a better choice is to vacate with your man on E. The blot you leave on K may be hit, but you will be in a good position to hit right back — and your four-point reception committee will be quite impressive.

VII
HITTING PLAYS

SCORE FOR THIS SECTION _82_

49

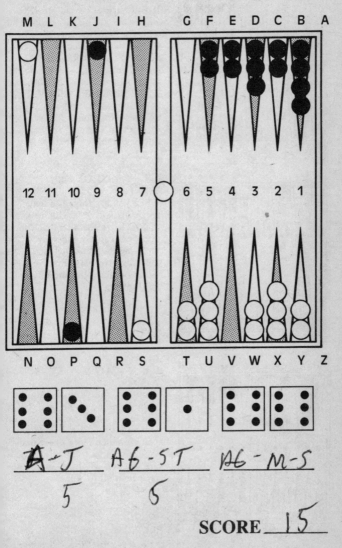

A-J
5

A6-5T
6

A6-M-S

SCORE __15__

127

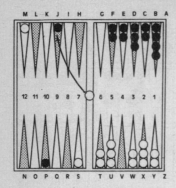

6-3 AG MP'=4
A–J'
If you hit Black's blot on J, you will be able to hit his second blot with either a 3 or 6 — 28 rolls. If, instead, you elect to hit the blot on P, you will have only half as many rolls — 14 — to hit Black's other blot. The play AG MP' is admittedly safer because A–J' does expose also to a double 4, but doubling the chances for hitting a second blot outweighs this extra shot.

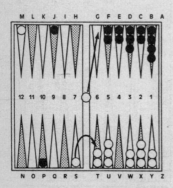

6-1 AG UV=2
AG ST
When you are forced to leave two blots, strive for duplication; that is, leave them so that your opponent can hit either by throwing the same number. With the suggested play, Black can hit either of your blots directly only by throwing a 3.

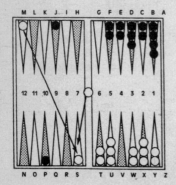

6-6 AG M–Y SY=3
A–S MS
Run, run, run! You will still be slightly behind in the race, but if you leave a man back on G, you will be even farther behind and you are much more likely than your opponent to be hit; if you are hit, you will have almost no chance at all to win.

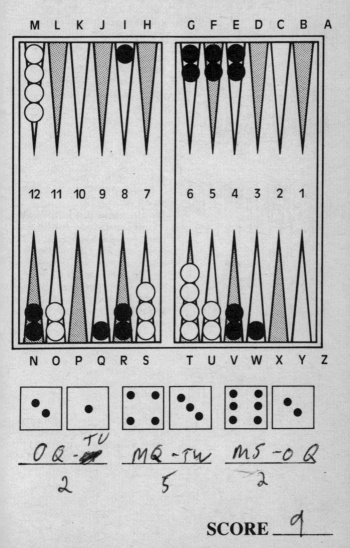

$$\underline{OQ - \overset{TU}{QR}}$$
2

$$\underline{MQ - TW}$$
5

$$\underline{MS - OQ}$$
2

SCORE 9

2-1   OQ' TU=2

MO TU

Do not hit a blot, for to do so
will leave you in an unstable
position. Besides, your opponent
has ample men back anyway.
Instead, work on bringing your
men in safely and building up an
inner board that will be better
than your opponent's.

4-3   SW' TW=4
         MPT=3

MQ' TW'

The alternative play of SW' TW
is quite satisfactory, but because
your opponent has only a
three-point inner board, a more
aggressive plan may be called
for. Hit both blots. If the blot
you leave in your inner board is
not hit in return, you will have
ample builders with which to
convert it to a point.

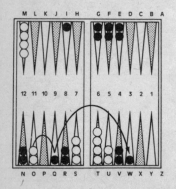

6-2   OU OQ=3
         MS MO=2
         M–U=2

OQ'W'

An aggressive play is again
called for even though there are
other alternatives which are
attractive.

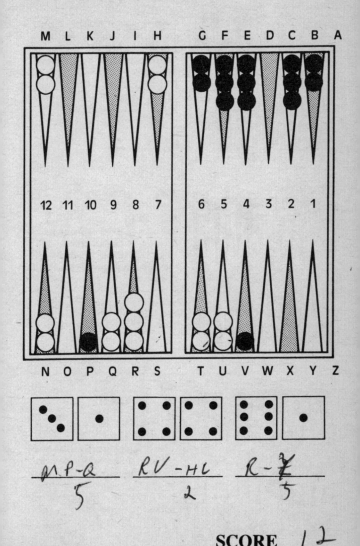

M L K J I H G F E D C B A

12 11 10 9 8 7   6 5 4 3 2 1

N O P Q R S   T U V W X Y Z

$$\frac{MP-Q}{5} \qquad \frac{RV-HL}{2} \qquad \frac{R-Z}{5}$$

SCORE _12_

51

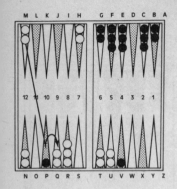

3-1 HI MP'=2
MP'Q
On first sight it looks like you are the underdog, but actually you are the favorite to win. You should play to hit and gradually contain your opponent's remaining men.

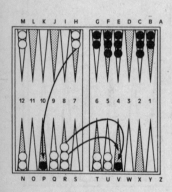

4-4 H-P2'=2
N-V2'=1
H-P' RV2'
Hit both blots. The man you leave on R cannot be hit on Black's next roll. Double 4 is a fine roll, although the game is far from over.

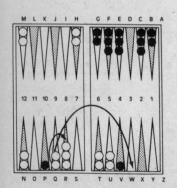

6-1 R-Y=5
HN HI=3
MS RS=3
NT NO=2
QW QR
This is a nightmare roll as you fail to hit either of Black's blots and can do little else. The least of all the evils is to pick a play that leaves no exposure, for your opponent's inner board is very solid.

52

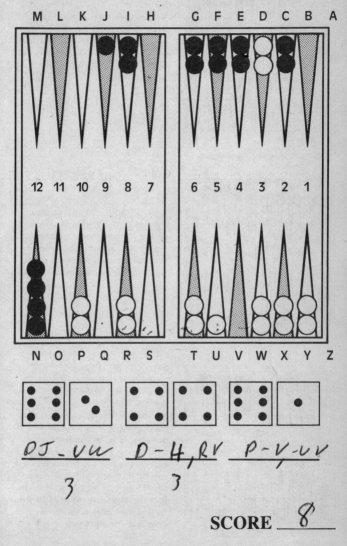

DJ-VW   D-H, RV   P-V,-UV
  3   3

SCORE 8

133

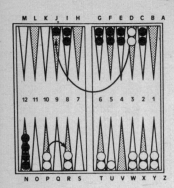

6-2   DJ' UW=3
DJ'L=2

DJ' PR
Your opponent's inner board deserves respect. If, however, you hit and then move your blot on U to W, you put the man out of play and give up on making a five-point board.

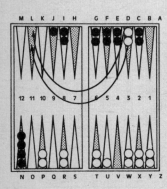

4-4   DH2 RV2=3
PT2 RV2=1

D–L2
Even without actually counting the position, casual observation makes it clear that if you run out with your brace of back men, you will be clearly ahead in the race. Get on your horse and go.

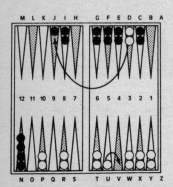

6-1   DJ' PQ=4
DJ'K=2
PV UV=2

DJ' UV
Hitting the blot is indicated, but playing the 1 is not nearly so obvious. The lesson here is in duplicating values. Because the blot you leave when you hit on J can be hit back with a 4, you should move up to V so that the blot there is also exposed to a 4. In this way only a throw of double 4 can hurt you.

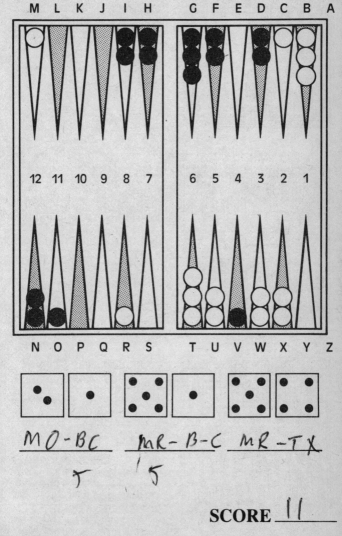

MO-BC

MR-B-C MR-TX

5   5

SCORE 11

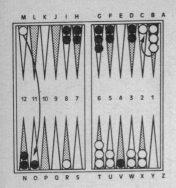

2-1   BC TV'=3
          BC RT=1

BC MO'
It is going to be difficult to gain
the timing you need for a
successful back game, but you
may be able to hit and contain
your opponent in your inner
board and then make his 4-point
and gradually escape.

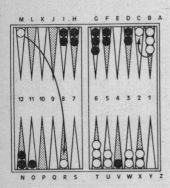

5-1   MR UV'=3
          BC TY=2

BC MR
Playing MR for the 5 is better
than moving to your own
1-point, even though your
objective is not really to get rid
of your blots.

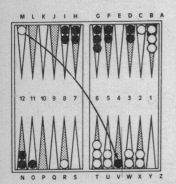

5-4   RV' TY=4
          MR TX=1

M–V'
The alternative of hitting and
also leaving two blots looks like
a mad play (RV' TY), but your
opponent in order to enter would
have to hit you and you would
succeed in getting the needed
fifth man back. However, by
making the suggested play, you
avoid slotting on the 1-point and
having to wait a long time to
make a point there.

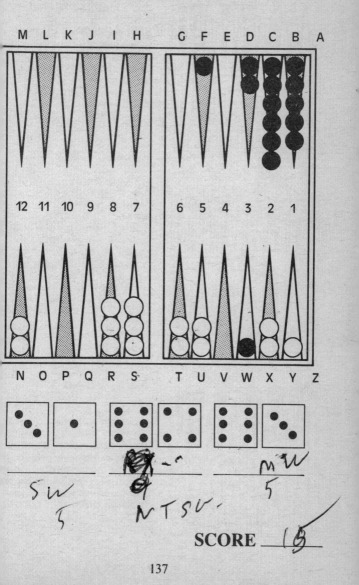

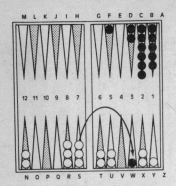

3-1
NQ ST=3
RU ST=2

S–W'

You must hit Black and try to push him back or else he may throw any 6 and escape. Even though you leave two blots in the process, there is no need to worry, for your opponent's inner-board defense has evaporated.

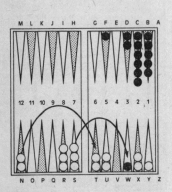

6-4
SY SW=4
NT NR=2

NT SW'

You must hit to try to contain your opponent; bringing a builder to your 6-point should come in very handy. The blot left on your 1-point does no harm. If it is hit, it can be entered easily and may be used for hitting Black's blot on F.

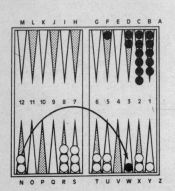

6-3
NT NQ=3
NQ SY=1

N–W'

Again, the tactic here is to hit t⦁ make it as difficult as possible for Black to escape. If one of your blots should be hit, you wi⦁ have no trouble entering and an⦁ man of yours put on the bar ma⦁ come in handy for hitting your opponent back.

55

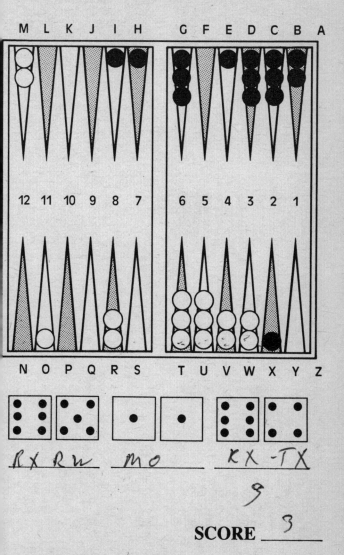

RX Rn   MO   KX -TX

9

SCORE 3

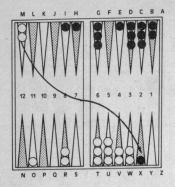

6-5   OT RX'=2

M–X'

You should hit. Your inner board is very good and if Black does not enter, you will be in a fine position to make a fifth inner point. If he does enter and hits you back, you may be able to hit the blot on his 4-point if he is forced to leave it. Playing OT RX' is not so effective because if Black throws 6-2, he will hit both your blots.

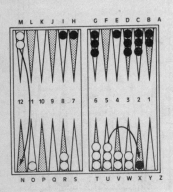

1-1   OP U–X'=5
O–Q WX2'=3
RS2 WX2'=3
MN UV WX2'=2

MN U–X'

There are many choices, but the best two selections leave your four consecutive points intact and start you on a fifth one. If you are hit, you will have a chance at hitting back and you may succeed in trapping Black for a few turns in your inner board when he does enter.

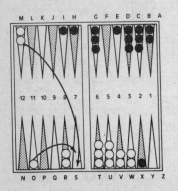

6-4   RX' TX=3
M–W=1

MS OS

Nothing can beat a prime, not even a five-point inner board with your opponent on the bar. By making a prime, you can then hit your opponent's blot on a subsequent turn and leave a blot intentionally. If he is forced to hit your blot in entering, you may be able to pick off one or more of his other blots as you enter from the bar.

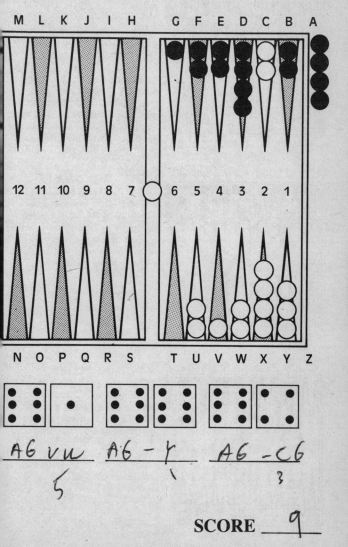

AG vu
5

AG - r
1

AG - CG
3

SCORE 9

56

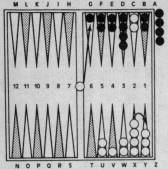

6-1 AG' VW=5
        AG'H=2

AG' XY

The 1 can be played unobtrusively within your inner board so that you will be able to cover your 4-point by throwing double 5 on your next roll; by staying on Black's 6-point, you place yourself 15 pips away from your own 4-point. The alternative — worth equal marks — is to move from your 4-point so you do not get hit and possibly gammoned.

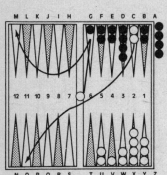

6-6 AG' C–O CI=4
        AG'–S CI=2

AG'M C–O

The play of AG'–S CI is too daring: You give yourself a chance to make a five-point board, but you leave two blots and risk being gammoned.

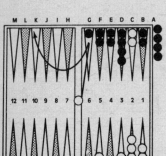

6-4 AG' CG=3

AG'K

By running to K, you are now able to make your 4-point on your next roll (if you are not hit) by throwing 6-5.

ADVANCED PLAYS

VIII
THE BACK GAME

SCORE FOR THIS SECTION _68_

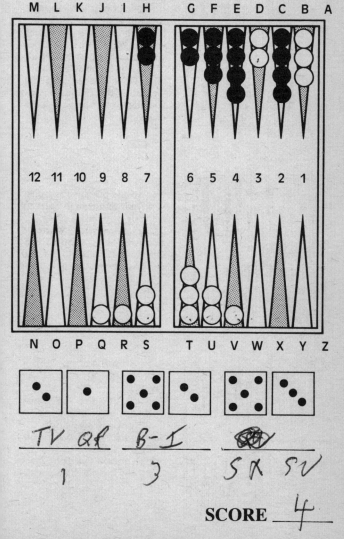

M L K J I H   G F E D C B A

12 11 10 9 8 7   6 5 4 3 2 1

N O P Q R S   T U V W X Y Z

TV Qℓ B-I
1   3   SX SV

SCORE 4

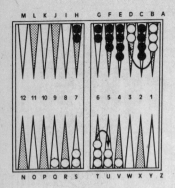

2-1 BD QR=4
QR TV=1
BD TU

It is always best in a classic back-game position to get your fifth man in escape position; if you do not, you risk messing up your inner board or being forced off the 3-point on subsequent rolls. TU is a better choice for the play of the 1 because it gives you more rolls from which to make your 4-point.

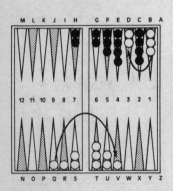

5-2 B–I=3
BD QV

You should postpone escaping with your fifth man in order to get your inner board ready. There are many rolls where Black will have to leave you a double shot; if he rolls 5-4, he will give you a quadruple shot!

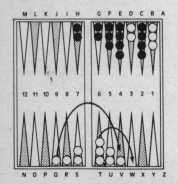

5-3 RW TW=2
QV RU=2
QV TW

The most effective way to play this roll is to make four consecutive points and slot a man on the 3-point. Such a play gives you a chance on your next turn to make a four-point inner board and possibly five points in a row.

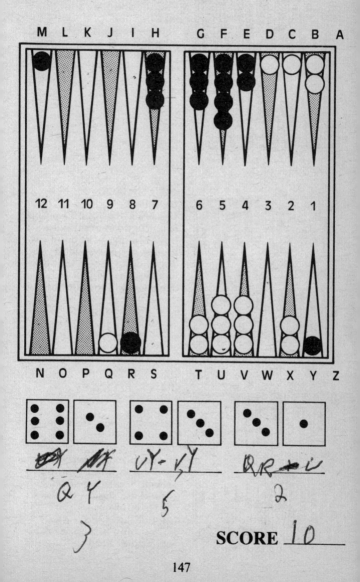

58

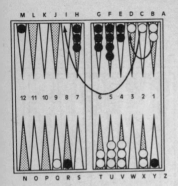

6-2 Q–Y'=3
QW UW=3

BD CI

Your timing is bad for a back game and Black has too many builders to pounce on you on D or C. Making a fifth point in your inner board also has to be abandoned.

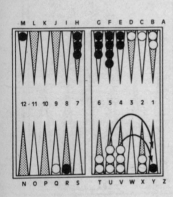

4-3 Q–X=1

UY' VY

This is a fine roll and it would be foolish to resort to any other play. Your five-point board will be most impressive and, if you can throw a 5 or 6 on your next turn to get one of your back men out, things will be easier for you.

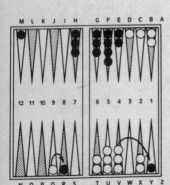

3-1 CD VY'=4
CD TW=2

QR' VY'

A double hit does your opponent a lot of damage from which he may never recover. If he should hit you on your 1-point, you can either try for a back game or, preferably, escape from his inner board as the chances are Black will not be able to get going full-steam again. Playing CD VY' sets up a back game but is not so strong a play.

148

59

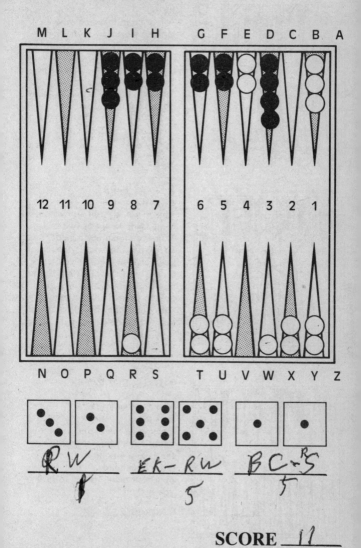

RW / ~~8~~

EK-RW / 5

BC-RS / 5

SCORE _11_

59

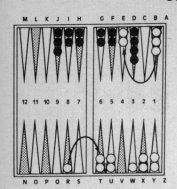

3-2   R–W=1
BE RT
A five-point inner board will
have to wait. If you make it
now, you will surely have to
wreck it at your next turn. Your
fifth back man in a back game
should always be placed on the
forward point so it can be used
for escaping.

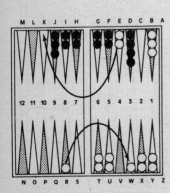

6-5 /   E–P=1
EK RW
This is a nasty roll and you have
to pick the lesser of two evils:
Running a man out is better than
wrecking your board. There is a
good chance the blot you leave
on the 4-point will be hit, but in
any case, you will always be
able to keep Black's 1-point, and
with your inner board preserved
you are in the game to the finish.

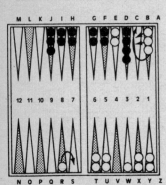

1-1   BC2 R–T=5
        BC R–U=3
        R–T UV2=1

BC3 RS
Occupying the 2- and 4-point is a
better back-game position than
the 1- and 4-point as there is
more likelihood of your
opponent being forced to give
you a shot.

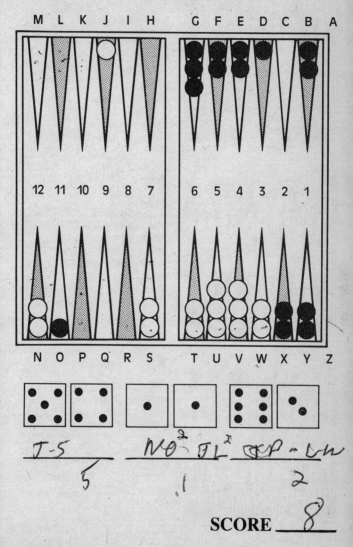

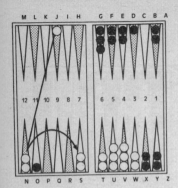

5-4   JO'S=3
JNS
You should not hit the blot or you will aid Black in giving him just the timing he would need for a good back game. If you ignore his blot, he will probably have to break up his inner board before you give him a shot.

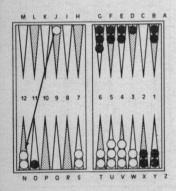

1-1   NO'P2=2
   JM NO'=2

J–N
You must avoid hitting Black's blot or you will put him into a sound back game; your best course of action is to run to safety.

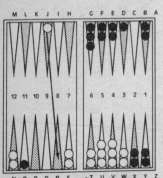

6-2   JP UW=2
   JP NP=1

J–R
It is too early for your opponent to hit you so you need not be concerned about landing on R. Furthermore, you may succeed in making a prime on your next throw which certainly would do no harm.

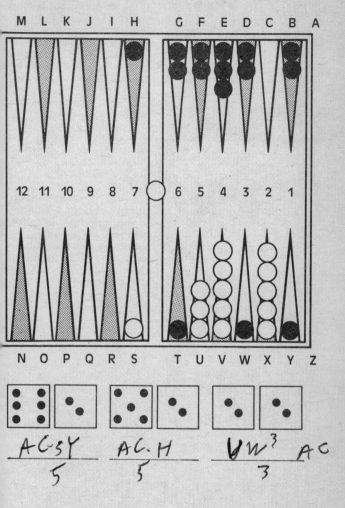

$$\frac{AC5Y}{5} \quad \frac{AC.H}{5} \quad \frac{VW^3}{3} \quad AC$$

SCORE __13__

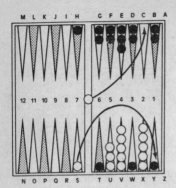

6-2   A–I=3
AC SY
In this situation, your opponent had a back game and hit you shortly before you were ready to bear off. If you play 6-2 to run to Black's 8-point, the blot you leave on your 7-point will be hit 27 out of 36 ways. The only possible tactic to employ to get back in the game is to hit the blot on your 1-point.

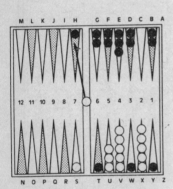

5-2   AC SX=2
A–H'
Entering and running to safety while simultaneously hitting appears tempting — and is the right play. While your blot on S is like an open wound, Black will have to use one of his dice for entering, so his odds of hitting you are reduced. The motto "when in doubt, hit" is valid here.

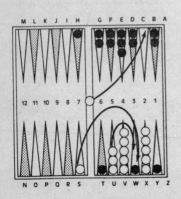

2-2   AC S–W'Y'=2
AC S–W' UW
This is a fine roll in which you enter, hit a blot and make four points in a row in your inner board — you cannot ask for more. The alternative play of hitting two blots is risky, for Black's five-point defense is just too overwhelming if you are hit back.

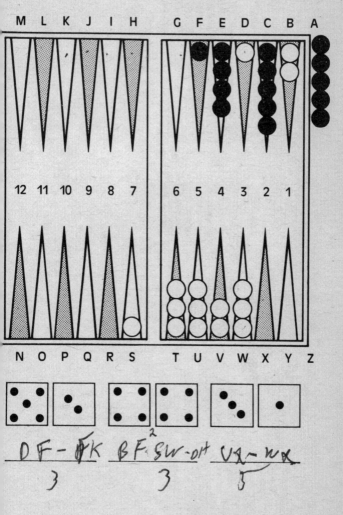

DF - FK   BF² SW-off   VX ~ WX
    3   3   5

SCORE 11

62

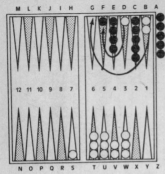

5-2 DF' SX=3
DF'K=3
DF' TY=1

BG DF'

Hitting the blot with the 2 is obvious. How to move your 5 is more subtle. Playing BG is sound so as to leave one man on Black's 1-point. Such a play will force him to hit you should he roll 3-1. You would then get a return shot, and if you hit a second man, you would be in a very commanding position indeed.

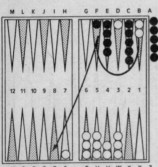

4-4 BF'–N DH=4
BF' D–P=2

BF'–R

Leaving a blot on your 8-point is preferred as it gives you a stronger attacking position. Black only has a two-point board, so you do not care if he throws 6-2 to hit you back.

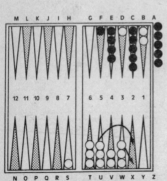

3-1 DG WX=1

UX WX

You are unable to hit, so the only thing left to do is get a better home defense ready for later.

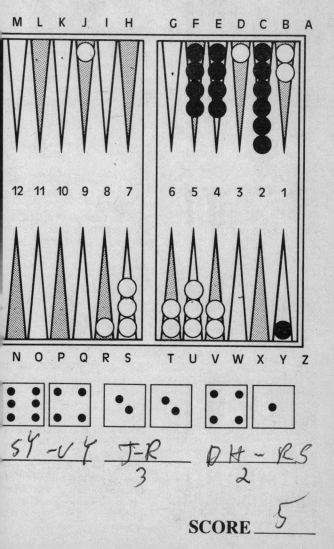

54 -UY   J-R   DH - RS
              3   2

SCORE 5

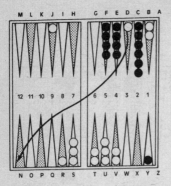

6-4   J–T=3
          BH JN=2
          DH JP=2

D–N

This position has occurred after White had a back game and hit Black. By moving all the way to your 12-point, you give yourself the best chance of making a solid block. Your goal is to keep Black's lone man from escaping.

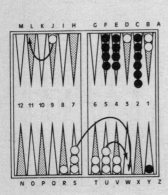

2-2   J–R=3
          RT S–W UW=2

JL S–W UW

Your best chance of making a prime is to make your 3-point and bring a lone man to L so that he is six pips — optimum distance — from your 8-point. Playing J–R is a reasonable play, but your chances for a prime are lessened.

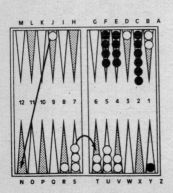

4-1   JN UV=4
          DH JK=3
          JK SW=2

JN ST

When you move JN, you make it easier to fill in your 8-point for subprime (five consecutive points). Playing JK SW, instead, is risky, for by slotting on your 3-point, you make it possible for Black to hit two of your blots with a 5-2 throw — and you could be in serious trouble if that happens.

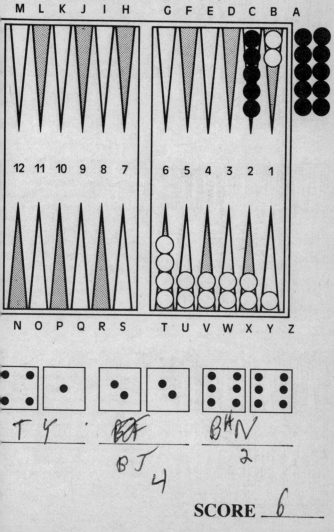

T Y   BCF
BJ
4

B*N
2

SCORE 6

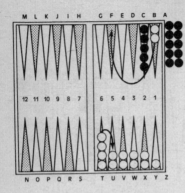

4-1 B–G=3
BF TU
Your best chance of hitting your opponent at the end when all his remaining men are piled on a single point is to leave a blot. Now if he throws a 1, he will be forced to hit you and leave a shot in return. Your play of TU gives you an extra builder to fill in your prime.

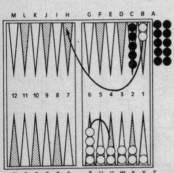

2-2 B–J=4
B–H TV
Leaving a blot is the best way to get Black to leave a blot himself, but in doing so you should escape with your other man from his inner board so that you will reduce his chances of scoring a backgammon. Playing B–J gives you a slightly better gammon save, but netting an extra builder for a closed board may be even better.

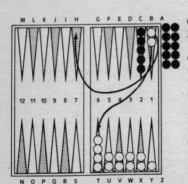

6-6 B–N2=2
B–T BH
You are forced to vacate your opponent's inner board so you must do so in the most effective way. Bearing in a man is better than leaving two men on your 12-point because you give yourself two extra rolls for avoiding gammon (double 5 and double 4) if your opponent does get off in two rolls.

ADVANCED QUIZZES

IX
THE MIDDLE GAME

SCORE FOR THIS SECTION _78_

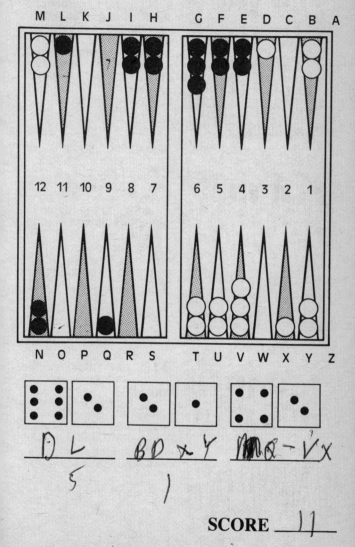

SCORE ___11___

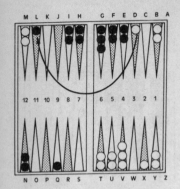

6-2 MS VX=1

D–L'

By hitting, you give your opponent a shot at hitting the blot on your 2-point, but there is no more attractive way to play this roll. If you are not hit back, you may be able to either make a fifth point or pick off Black's other blot.

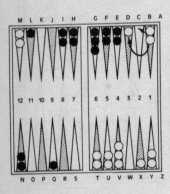

2-1 BD VW=2
BD XY=1

BD BC

If you play the 2 to your own 2-point, you will have no convenient play for the 1. Thus, it is better to make your opponent's 3-point and save improving your inner board for later.

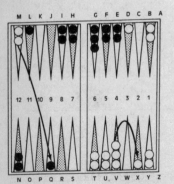

4-2 BD MQ'=1
BD TX=1

MQ' VX

This is your best throw, but it still may not ultimately turn the game around. You might as well hit and make a fifth inner point. If you can escape soon with a back man, there may be hope.

66

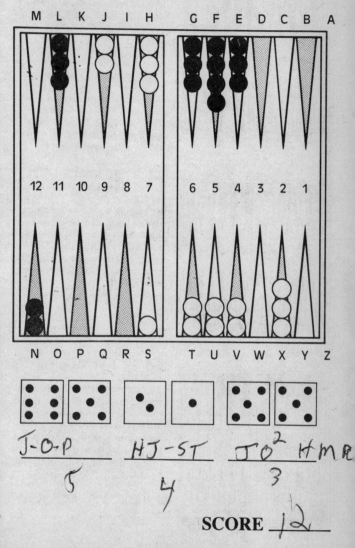

J-O-P
5

HJ-ST
4

J-O² HMR
3

SCORE 12

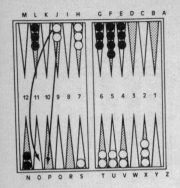

6-5   H–S=3
JP JO
Moving a man straight down
from your opponent's 7-point to
your own 7-point (H–S) is
tempting, but you would risk
leaving a blot in your opponent's
outer board before he leaves you
a blot. By clearing both men off
his 9-point, instead, you
establish three builders in your
own outer board which can be
used for improving your inner
board and for stalling; now Black
will have to leave a shot first.

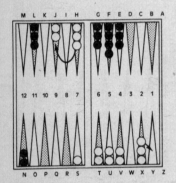

2-1   HJ ST=4
        H–K=1
HJ XY
By playing your 2 to J, you are
able to keep your basic position
intact for a while and still have a
man with which to run. The 1 is
better played to your 1-point in
an attempt to make a five-point
inner board.

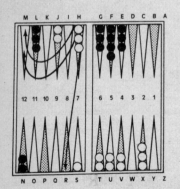

5-5   H–R JO2=3
H–R HM2
The recommended play is a little
smoother than H–R JO2: If you
throw more high numbers, you
are less likely to leave blots in
running to your outer board and
you may be able to outrace your
opponent more easily by running
to M.

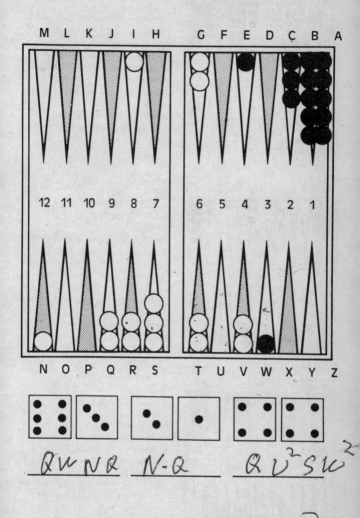

67

QWNR N-Q QV²SW²

SCORE 2

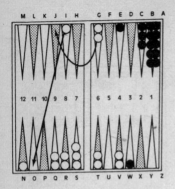

6-3 G–P=4
N–W'=1

GJ IO

There is no need to hit as Black cannot escape unless he throws 6-2 or 5-2 and even then he would be wide open. Your aim now is to build a prime to contain Black's last man. If you can do so, you will be able to bring all your men in, avoid gammon and eventually win the game.

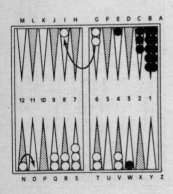

2-1 NO SU=5
G–J=3
IK NO=2

GI NO

The 2 is played so that if you throw double 6, you will make a prime. The suggested move for the 1 is to go to your 11-point for two reasons: You improve your chances for a prime, and if Black throws 6-2, he will be forced to hit you in escaping and you will have a shot at hitting his inner blot. The alternative play, NO SU, is excellent, too.

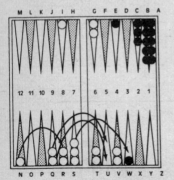

4-4 IM QU2 SW'=4
QU2 SW2'=2

NR QU2 SW'

By choosing this option, you make a subprime, hit your opponent and create a blot in your inner board. If your blot is hit, you get a shot at Black's other blot; if your blot is not hit, you will try to make a prime.

68

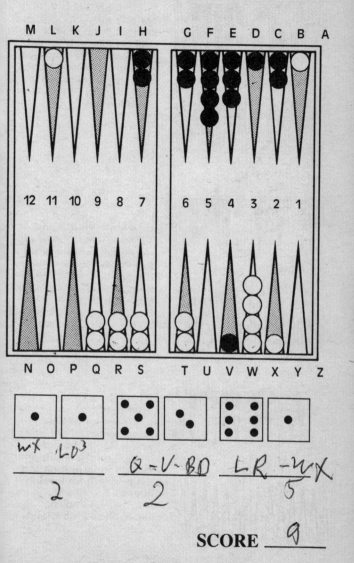

SCORE 9

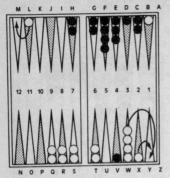

1-1   S–V' WX=4
          S–U2=2

LM W–Y XY

Double 1 in this instance is a mediocre roll and is best handled by making a third inner point. Alternatively you can take a more aggressive line and hit while filling in your 2-point. It is almost a toss-up.

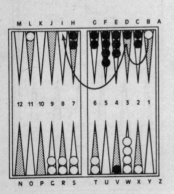

5-2   BD' SX=3
          QV'X=2

BD'I

Using your lone back man to hit the blot is sound practice and you should continue running with that man at the expense of leaving a blot in your own board. You succeed in getting him out from the back court and you keep the four consecutive points in your middle area intact.

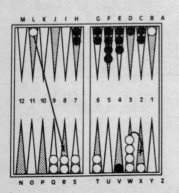

6-1   RX RS=2
LR WX

There is no need to move both men from your 8-point as you have a surplus of men on the 3-point that can be used for making your 2-point. By moving the man on L, your opponent will be able to run to safety if he throws a 6, but his blot in his inner board will still be vulnerable unless he also throws a 1 or 2.

69

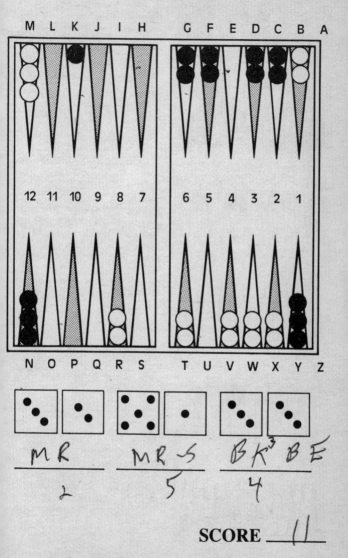

MR
___
2

MR~S
___
5

BK³ BE
___
4

SCORE ___ 11

69

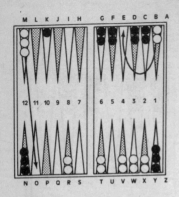

3-2 MP RT=4
M–R=2

BE MO
Because Black has no builders in his inner board, you can split your back men. Placing a man on E may hinder your opponent from entering his outer board at will.

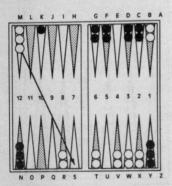

5-1 R–X=2
M–S

Placing a man on your 7-point exposes to a direct hit but outweighs the alternative of moving a man out of play to your 2-point. Also, you may succeed in making your 7-point on your next throw and this will keep your opponent fenced in.

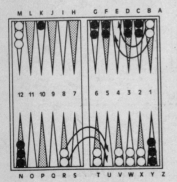

3-3 B–K' BE=4
B–K' MP=3
B–H2=3
BE MP3=1

BE2 RU2
There are many good plays here and the most attractive of these is to advance to your opponent's 4-point and make your own 5-point. The blot on K can wait as Black's unfavorable position will yield more blots very soon.

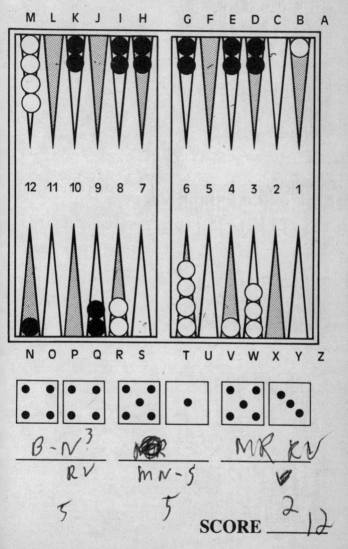

$$\frac{B-N^3}{RV}$$

5

$$\frac{MR}{MN-5}$$

5

MR RV

✓

2

SCORE _12_

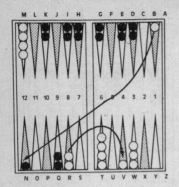

4-4   BF RV TX2=1
B–N' RV
From the upper-right corner of
the board to the lower-left corner
is a long distance of 12 pips, but
double 4 makes the trip in spite
of Black's six scattered points.
This is a dramatic roll that puts
you back in the game.

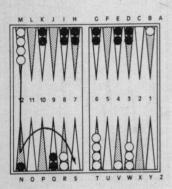

5-1   MRS=3
        MR TU=1
MN'S
Some aggressive action is called
for in an effort to turn the game
around. The best idea is hitting
rather than bypassing Black's
blot on N.

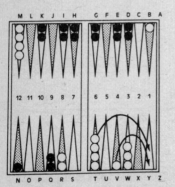

5-3   M–U=2
        MR MP=2
TY VY
There are aggressive and
imaginative alternatives, but the
soundest play is simply to make
your 1-point and see what
develops.

71

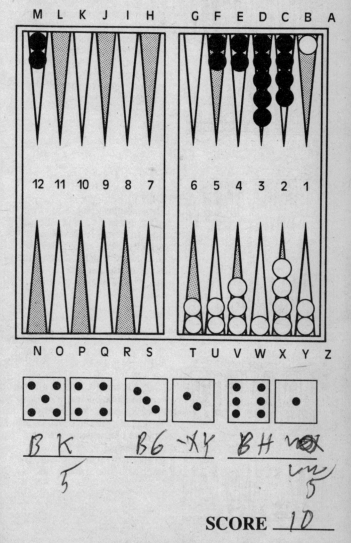

BK
5

B6 ~XY

BH ~~VOX~~
~~VW~~
5

SCORE 10

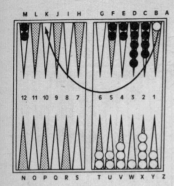

5-4   BG TX=3
          TY TX=2

B–K

The alternative of breaking up your 6-point is not called for: Your inner-board defense would be greatly damaged and you would still have a long trip home from Black's territory. By running, you give yourself the best chance of winning.

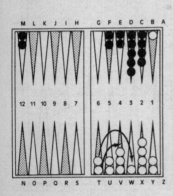

3-2   TW VX=4
          VY WY=3

TW TV

The smoothest play is to move off your 6-point as the race is close to even. By playing as suggested, you make a five-point inner-board which will come in handy if you can luckily hit as Black bears in his last men.

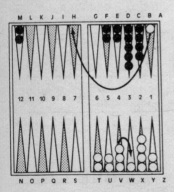

6-1   B–I=3

BH VW

Your 6 is forced, but there is no need to move one extra pip to Black's 8-point. You opponent has exactly the same chance of hitting a blot whether it is four or five spaces away (15 ways), so play the 1 more productively and make your inside prime.

72

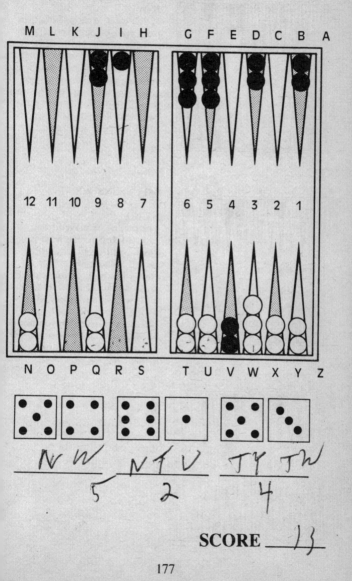

NW
—
5

NTV
—
2

JY JW
—
4

SCORE ___ 13

177

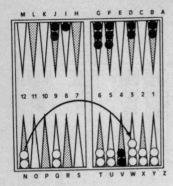

5-4 TY TX=1
N–W

If you elect to move both men from your 6-point, you will not leave a shot — for now, that is. It is best to get one man from your 12-point all the way home; your opponent can hit the blot you leave with only five possible throws. This blot, if not hit, will be in excellent shape to reach safety on your next roll.

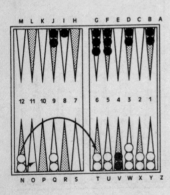

6-1 NT WX=2
QW QR=1
NT NO

The 6 must be played from your 12-point, for to play from your 9-point will result in a direct shot. The question is how to cope with the 1. If you leave the man on your 12-point, Black can hit it with five rolls (6-2, 5-3, 4-4); if you move it one pip closer, paradoxically, you can be hit with only four rolls (6-1, 4-3) as a throw of 5-2 does no damage to you!

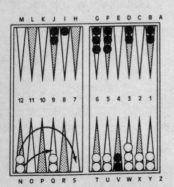

5-3 TY TW=4
Q–Y=2
NS NQ

If you move from your outer board, you will have to leave a direct shot; but to do this is a shade better than breaking your 6-point and probably having to leave a direct shot later.

ADVANCED QUIZZES

X
WHEN OPPONENT
IS ON THE BAR

SCORE FOR THIS SECTION 58.5

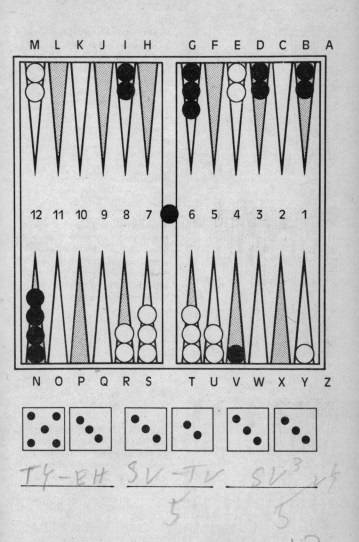

TY-EH SV-TV SV³ ¥¥
5 5

SCORE 12

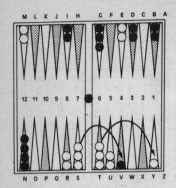

5-3   E–M=3
SV' TY
In situations like this, it pays to be aggressive and think in terms of a possible gammon. After you hit and cover on your 1-point, your inner board will be much improved and you will have two of Black's men on the bar; unless he hits you on your 4-point, he may never get back in the game.

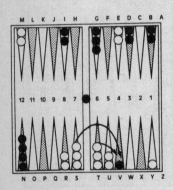

3-2   TV'Y=2
SV' TV
The alternative play of TV'Y is not so good. By playing as suggested, you make a valuable subprime and even if you are hit on the 1-point, you should have little difficulty in entering and bringing the man around.

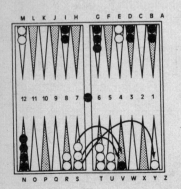

3-3   M–V' SV=4
           EH2 SV2'=2

SV2' S–Y
This play, in which you hit another blot and make two points, is a little better than making a subprime and leaving a blot (M–V' SV).

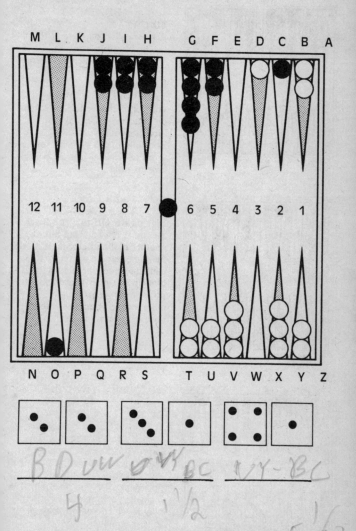

SCORE ____

74

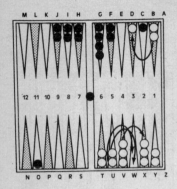

2-2 BD2 UW2=4
BD2 TV2=3

BD UW2 VX
A poor roll. You have little choice but to vacate your 5-point. The problem is whether or not to leave one man on Black's 1-point. You should do so for two reasons: You give yourself a chance to hit his blot on your next turn and you increase your chances of escaping by 100 percent, for now a roll of either 6-1 or 6-3 will get one man out.

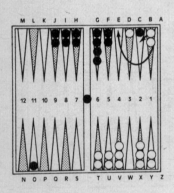

3-1 BE DE=3
BE BC'
Playing BE DE to make Black's 4-point is not bad, but hitting another blot and placing just one man in escape position is sounder. Your three consecutive blots in his inner board should pose no problems as it will be quite awhile before he enters both men from the bar.

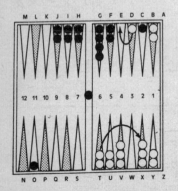

4-1 TX TU=5
BC' TX=2

DE TX
It looks like a crazy play, but 4-1 is such an awful roll that some improvisation may be called for. You at least succeed in placing a man in escape position on your opponent's 4-point. The play TX TU gets equal marks as it is the play in which you are least likely to be gammoned.

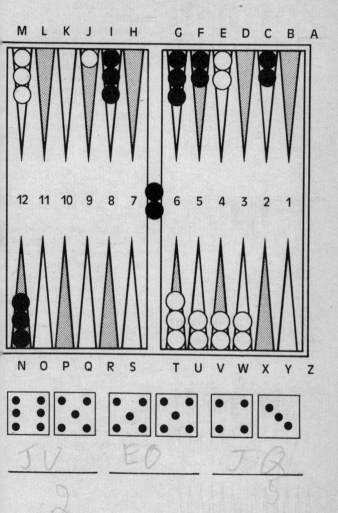

SCORE _____

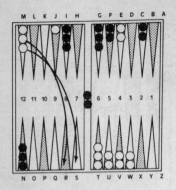

6-5   J–U=2
         JO MS=2

MS MR

When two of your opponent's men are on the bar, you can be very liberal in leaving outside blots because he must use both his dice for entering. The two builders you post on your 8- and 7-point will be most effective in making a five-point board or in rehitting your opponent.

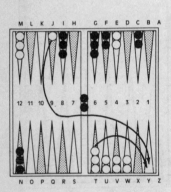

5-5   M–W MR2=5
         MR3 EJ=2

J–Y TY

Did you miss seeing this move? It is the old "15-5" play and is often overlooked. Playing M–W MR2 is also very sound, the theory being to avoid advancing men all the way to the 1-point when you can post more builders and aim for the 2-point.

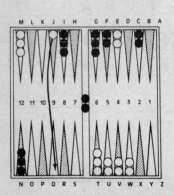

4-3   MQ MP=2

J–Q

Because you are unable to post two additional builders in direct range of your 2-point, you might as well move from 9-point to 9-point.

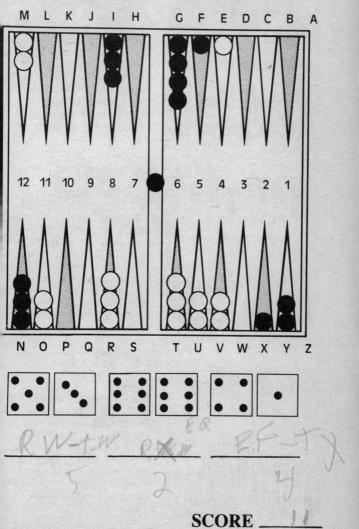

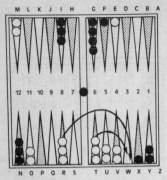

5-3   E–M=2
OT OR=1
MR MP=1

RW TW

By making a fourth point in your inner board, you make it much more difficult for your opponent to enter, and by keeping your lone man back, you give yourself the option of hitting another blot. You will hit only if your opponent is not able to set up a good back-game position.

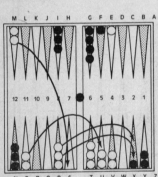

6-6   MS2 RX2'=4
E–Q RX2'=2
OU2 RX2'=1

MS OU RX2'

Your tactics are to make it very difficult for Black to get a back game going. By hitting the blot on your 2-point and covering, in addition to establishing two extra builders, you will be able to hit your opponent if he dares to enter a man on your 3-point. Playing MS2 RX2' is almost as effective.

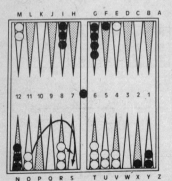

4-1   EF' TX'=4
RS TX'=2

OS RS

This is a powerful roll and making your 7-point is the soundest play, as Black will probably not be able to hold a strong back game. Hitting two blots (EF' TX') is aggressive and gives you a chance at gammon, but the alternative of making a subprime is more constructive.

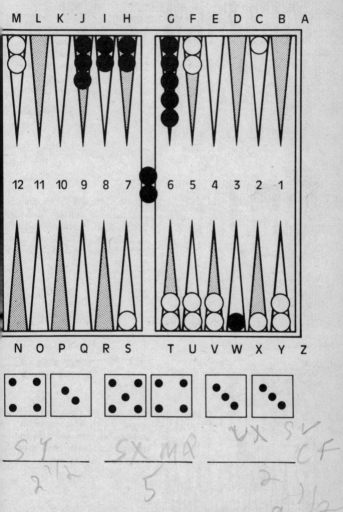

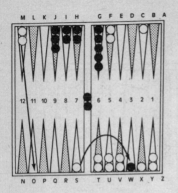

4-2   CE SW'=4
CE MQ=3
MQ MO=2

MO SW'

You can let out all the stops on this one as Black has no inner board and two men on the bar. If he does not enter and you throw a 1, you can make a five-point board and gammon should be yours.

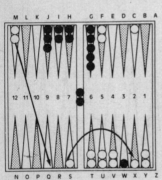

5-4   MR SW'=3
MQ SX

Playing MR SW' is imaginative but the more conservative play is preferred as it nets a five-point inner board. Unless your opponent tosses a miracle double 3, he is finished.

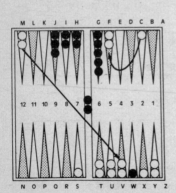

3-3   CF MP TW2'=4
CF M–S MP=2

CF M–V

By moving a man on M nine pips, you give yourself an extra builder with which to either make your 2-point or hit the remaining blot on your 3-point.

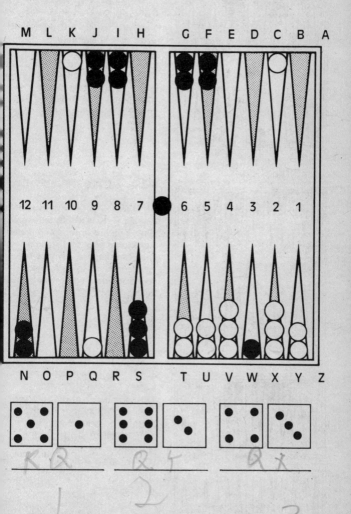

SCORE _____

78

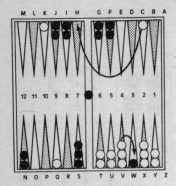

5-1   KP VW'=4
               K–Q=1

CH VW'

Your opponent's board is very weak so you can play aggressively and go for the gammon. After you hit Black, the blot on Q should stay where it is as it cannot be hit on Black's next roll; it will be more effective there for making your 3-point.

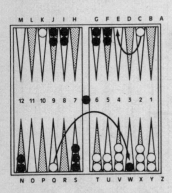

6-2   C–K=3
               QW'Y=2

CE QW'

Playing C–K is a safe but weak play. You are in total command and should play on for gammon. Hit! Use the 2 to advance to your opponent's 4-point with your back man so he will be able to exit more easily.

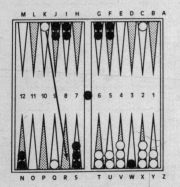

4-3   KO QT=3
K–R

This is not a good roll, but you should still play it aggressively. If Black does not enter, you will be in excellent shape to hit his blot on the 3-point — and perhaps make a prime.

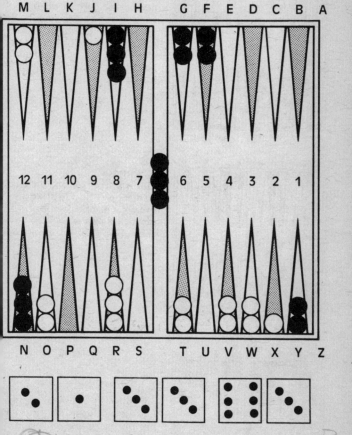

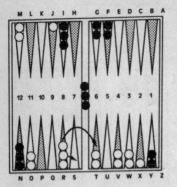

2-1   J–M=1
RT RS

Your plan is to establish two more builders which will be effective in covering your 2-point or making your 5-point. When your opponent has two or more men on the bar and no defense, you can be very lenient about leaving blots.

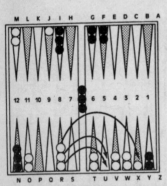

3-3
R–X RU2

This is a super roll and there is no other play than to make a five-point inner board. A gammon is now guaranteed unless Black hits you toward the end.

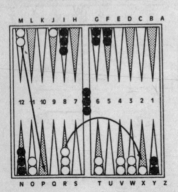

6-3   OU RU=3
          JM RX=2

MP RX

Making your 5-point is fine but not at the expense of leaving the blot on the 2-point. If that blot is hit, you would lose the tempo you need to really keep the heat on your opponent.

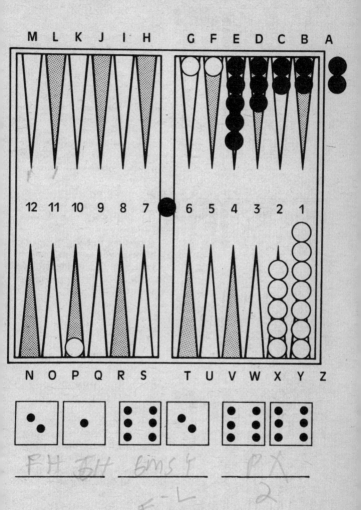

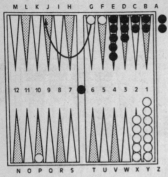

2-1   F–I=3
            FH GH=1

G–J

This position is the result of a marathon struggle in which White has repeatedly hit Black's 15th man but was unable to contain it because White's inner-board defense disappeared a long time ago. The best play is for you to move as indicated so that if you throw double 6 on your next turn, you will safely make your 4-point, or if you throw double 5, you will make your 5-point.

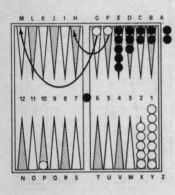

6-2   FL GI=5
            G–O=4
            P–X=2

FH GM

It is best not to bring the man on P home as you need as many outside men as possible deployed to hit Black as he tries to come around.

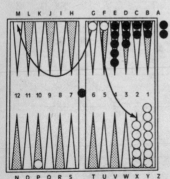

6-6   F–X PV=2
            G–Y PV=2

F–X GM

This is a biggie and it is time to think in the direction of getting all your men safely home and winning the race. Playing GM gives you a good shot at hitting Black one more time as he heads around the track.

ADVANCED QUIZZES

XI
THE PRIME

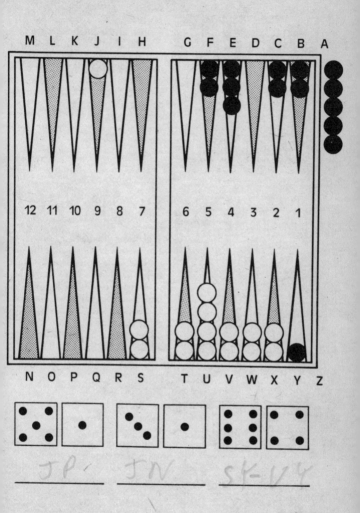

SCORE _____

81

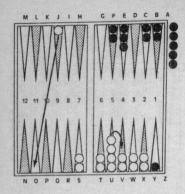

5-1   J–P=2
JO UV
Your tactic is to give yourself
the best chance to hit Black's
blot while keeping your prime
intact. By hitting, you hope he
will hit you back and have to
leave a shot in his inner board in
playing his other number. If you
can hit a second blot, you give
yourself a good chance for
victory.

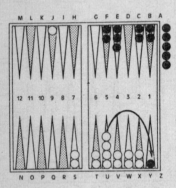

3-1   JM UV=2
           J–N=1

U–Y'
Whenever you have a prime, you
can leave a blot in front of it —
if there is no worry about getting
trapped behind a block of your
opponent's if you are hit. You
hope your opponent will hit you
and leave a shot in playing his
other number. Here Black will
do just that if he rolls 4-1 — not
a likely event, but you have
nothing to lose by trying.

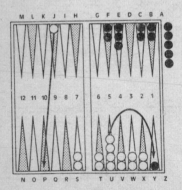

6-4   SY' UY=3
           J–T=1

JP UY'
Playing SY' UY is not so strong
a move because you would make
an inside prime and stop your
opponent from rolling. Actually
you want him to roll so that he
may eventually leave a shot that
you could then hit.

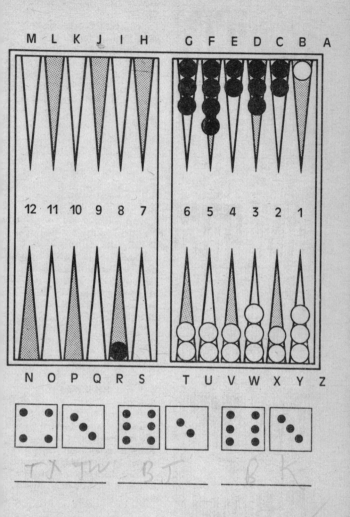

SCORE _____

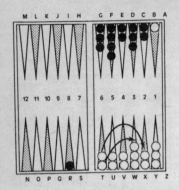

4-3   UY UX=2
TX TW
Time to get the wrecking crew
here. You are forced to break up
your inner board and the best
method is to strip the highest
point first.

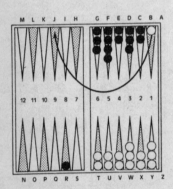

6-2   BH WY=3
B–J
Your 6 is forced and you should
play the 2 to move even farther
ahead. Your runner will
admittedly be in a worse spot to
hit Black's blot if he fails to
throw high enough to fly past you
but in a better position to get by
on the next roll and win the
race.

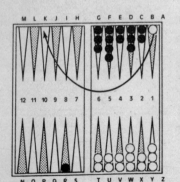

6-3   BH TW=1
B–K
Rather than break your board,
you should move to K. You will
still be able to have a shot at
Black if he does not throw 8 or
higher. Another reason for not
wasting the 3 is that if you are
unable to hit, you may still win
the race.

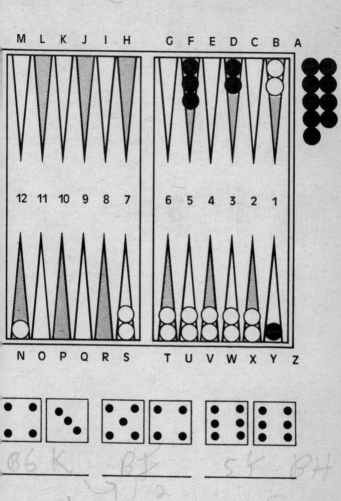

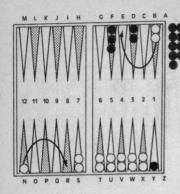

4-3   N–U=2
        B–I=1

BE NR

Split your back men! There is no worry about being hit as you will be able to rehit. If you can hit a second man, you will be the favorite to win the game. When you split here, your opponent will leave a shot with more rolls, too, and he leaves a double shot with a throw of 3-2 — and a rare triple shot with throws of 4-3 or 4-1.

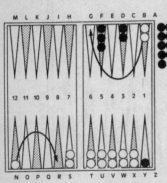

5-4   N–W=3

BG NR

Rather than advance the man on N nine pips, you should move one of your back men. Now Black will be forced to leave a shot with more rolls and in some cases, he leaves you a multiple shot.

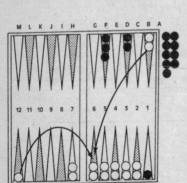

6-6   B–T SY'=2
        BH NT SY2'=1
        B–N SY2'=1

B–T NT

A big roll, but you are still able to leave a man back to hit a blot that Black is likely to leave on his next roll. You must not make your inside prime or even hit Black on the 1-point and leave a blot; the idea is to force Black to move on his next throw.

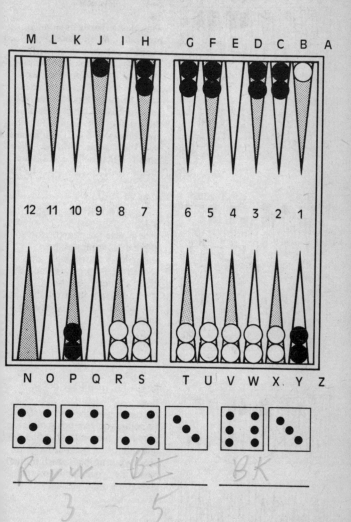

R v w   B I   B K

3 — 5

SCORE 13

84

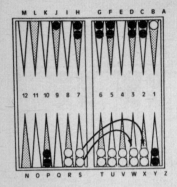

5-4 RW RV=3
SX SW
This classic backgammon problem, long cherished by experts, depicts one of the few situations where it is correct to break an interior point rather than the highest point. If you break from the 8-point, you will have to leave a direct shot on the 7-point on your next turn if you roll 6-5 or 6-4. If you break from the 7-point, however, there is no roll that will force a direct shot.

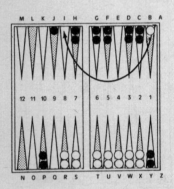

4-3 SW SV=2
          RV RU=1
B–I
Flee or else you may be forced to break your impressive blockade. You will have to dodge bullets to get around from Black's 8-point, but that is fine: If you do not enter from the bar, you will keep your superprime intact.

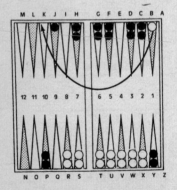

6-3 BE RX=2
B–K
By running all the way to the 10-point, you risk being hit, but if you are put on the bar and do not enter, you will not have to break your prime — and, in the meantime, your opponent may give you a shot later on.

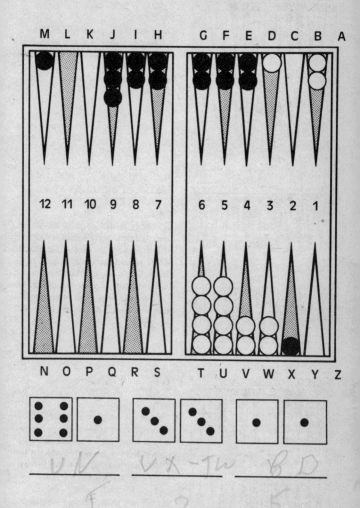

SCORE ____

85

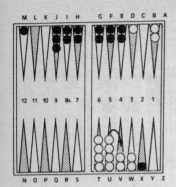

6-1 TU — =3
WX' — =2

UV —
Only your 1 is playable. Hitting the blot on your 2-point to attempt a back game is bold, but it is a desperation tactic; it could backfire and you may be gammoned.

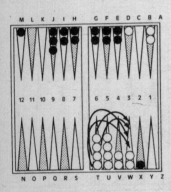

3-3 TW2 UX2'=3
TW2 VY2=2

TW4
This play is designed to avoid being gammoned. The alternative of hitting and making a five-point board would have merit only if Black throws a 1 right away and fails to throw a 6 for a few turns. This would then give you only a remote chance of getting back in the game.

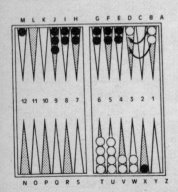

1-1 T–X'=3
V–X' W–Y=1

B–D2
This is a safe play and once again your plan is to concentrate on avoiding losing a double game rather than winning. Playing T–X' is a bold play in which you hope for Black to enter right away on your 2-point; you may get a back game going if Black throws high numbers repeatedly.

208

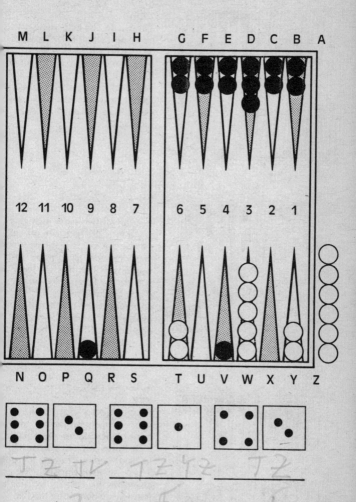

SCORE 13

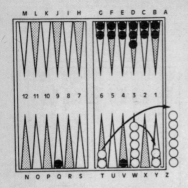

6-2   TZ TV'=3
TZ WY

The 6 is forced and whether you hit or not with the 2, there will be 13 rolls with which your opponent can hit you. If you do hit, there is a chance Black will be unlucky and not enter, but there is a greater chance he will enter on your 2-point and wait for a shot.

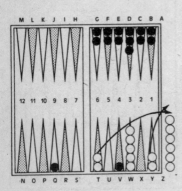

6-1   TZ TU=4
TZ YZ

Bearing off two more men gives you a total of eight men off and eight is the magic number: When your opponent has a prime and you have borne off eight men, you are the favorite to win even if you are hit. Playing TZ TU does reduce the number of rolls by one with which your opponent can hit you, but you get only one man off.

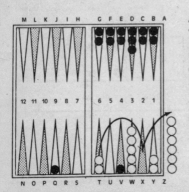

4-2   TV'Z=2
TXZ

If you play TV'Z, you place your opponent on the bar and he can hit your blot on the 6-point with 16 rolls; if you do not hit, he can hit you with only 13 rolls. Thus, you give yourself a better chance in this case by refusing to put your opponent on the bar.

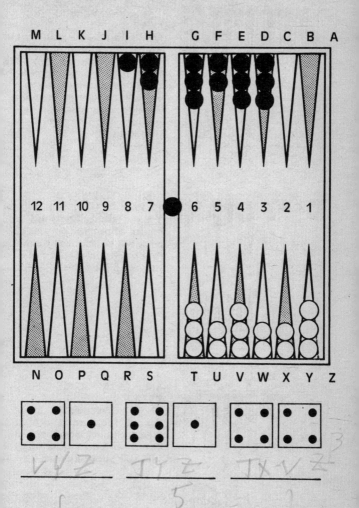

VYZ   JYZ   JXVZ
 1   5   1

SCORE 7

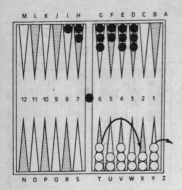

4–1   T–Y=1
VZ YZ=1

TX YZ
The standard technique in bearing off is to leave an even number of men on your two highest points. If you play VZ YZ to bear off two men, you will leave an odd number of men on your highest points and you may have to leave a shot on your next roll.

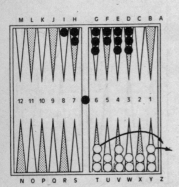

6-1   TZ VW=4
TZ YZ
You can take the liberty of bearing off two men for your prime will be intact and you will have an even number of men on your two highest points.

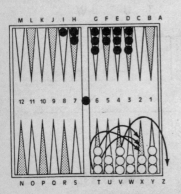

4-4   TX VZ3=1
TX3 VZ
This is the only safe way to play this roll. The other option of bearing off three men from your 4-point will leave a space which will make you shot-prone.

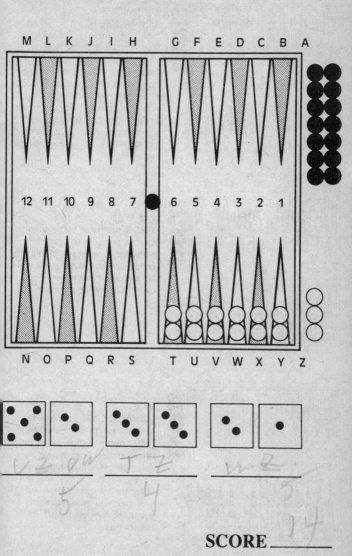

SCORE _____

88

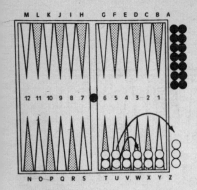

5-2 UZ XZ=3
UZ UW
In this game White hit Black's
last man at the last minute and
has averted gammon and
backgammon. The odds are long
on winning after your opponent
has borne off 14 men, but there
is a chance nevertheless. You
win this kind of game by being
lucky — and by having your
inner-board defense as strong as
possible to keep your opponent
out.

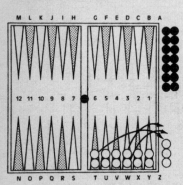

3-3 T–Z2=4
UX2 WZ2=1
T–Z WZ2
You should bear off as many
men as possible in order to have
a chance of winning. If Black
enters on the 6-point, you will be
hit and will have a chance to
catch him on the rebound.

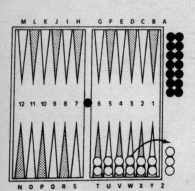

2-1 XZ YZ=4
TV TU=2
W–Z
Playing XZ YZ is imaginative
and has merit, but a slightly
better move is to bear off only
one man and keep a nice
five-point board. Chances are
very good that Black will not
enter on his next throw and this
will give you an opportunity to
get more men off before he
comes on.

214

ADVANCED QUIZZES

XII
VARIOUS
POSITIONAL PLAYS

SCORE FOR THIS SECTION _75_

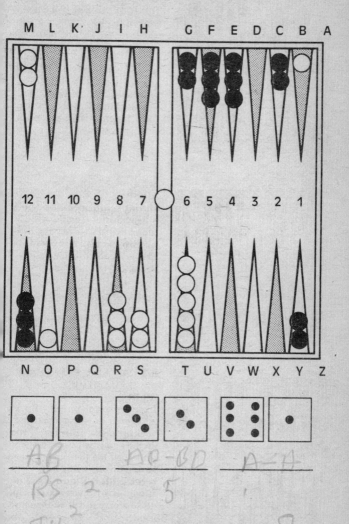

AB _____   AC-BD _____   A-A _____
RS 2   5   ,
TV 2

SCORE 8

89

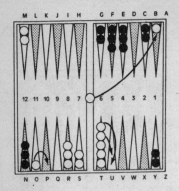

1-1 AB RS TU2=2
AB OP TU2
This is an excellent roll and not difficult to play. You enter your man from the bar and make your 5-point, of course. The last 1 of your roll should be played to bring a man from your 11-point to your 10-point. You succeed in being only six pips away from your 4-point and make it that much easier to make that point on your next roll.

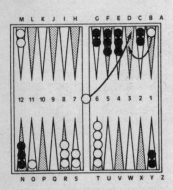

3-2 AD OQ=2
AD BD
Making your opponent's 3-point is much better than the alternative play of leaving two men bare in his inner board. This is a good roll and greatly stabilizes your position.

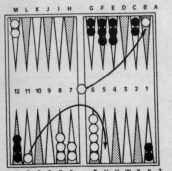

6-1 AB MS=3
A–H=1

AB OU
Exposing a man on your 5-point is superior to taking a man out to your opponent's 7-point. If you do the latter, you will be hit about half the time and you may have difficulty in entering because Black's inner board is strong. If you must leave a blot, do so where it will do the most good.

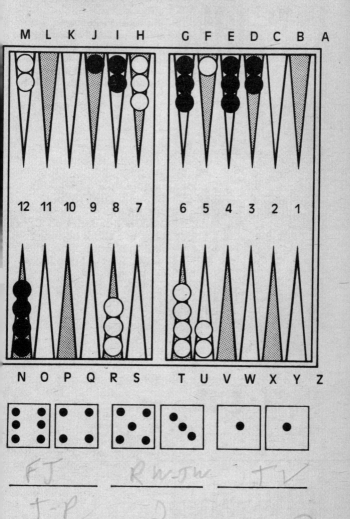

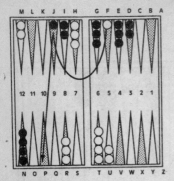

6-4 RX TX=1
FJ'P
Hitting and escaping to your own outer board is a strong play; you are in danger only if your opponent also throws 6-4 and hits you back. Making your 2-point, alternatively, would be a weak move.

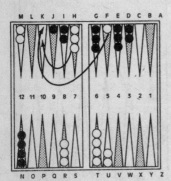

5-3 RW TW=2
  H–P=1
FK HK
Making your opponent's 10-point gets your blot to safety and stabilizes your position. This play is superior to just making your own 3-point.

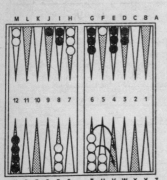

1-1 RS2 T–V=3
  RS3 TU=1
T–V2
You must make your 4-point here as it will give you a three-point inner board; now your opponent will have to think twice about hitting your blot on F — unless he can also cover when he hits.

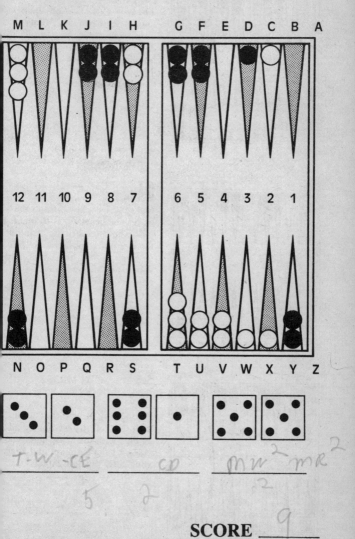

SCORE 9

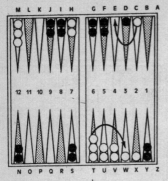

3-2 MO TW=2
CE TW
The play of the 3 is obvious:
One of your two inner blots
must be covered. That leaves the
2, which is best handled by
hopping over Black's blot to his
4-point. Now that man will be
able to escape more readily.

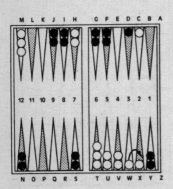

6-1 CD' —=2
WX —
Only the 1 is playable and the
better choice by far is to make a
four-point board rather than hit
the blot and expose yourself to
so many return shots. You may
succeed in hitting your
opponent's blot on your next
throw anyway.

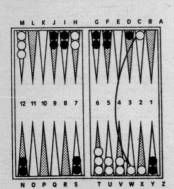

5-5 M–W MR2=2
       H–R2=1
C–W
All the way around the bases
with this roll! By advancing all
20 pips with the same man, you
make a valuable point and keep
your outer position intact.

92

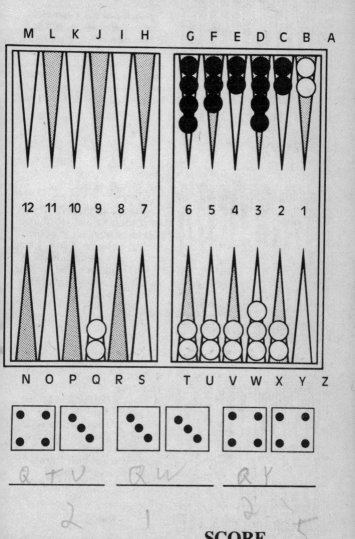

Q + V

Q W

Q Y

2

1

2

SCORE 5

223

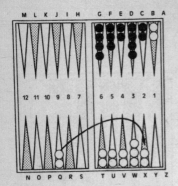

4-3   QU QT=2
Q–X
Timing is the major consideration in this problem. If you bear in both men and then throw a 6 on your next turn, you will lose your ace-point back game. By keeping a man on Q, you stall and will be able to stay back on the 1-point an extra turn or two.

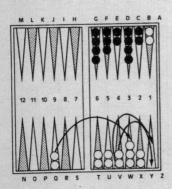

3-3   Q–W2=1
Q–W VY2
You should keep a man in your outer board so that you will be able to maintain the ace-point back game longer. Black will not have to give a shot at his next turn no matter what he throws, so it is vital that you stay back as long as you can.

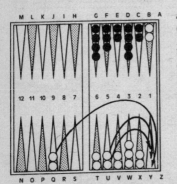

4-4   Q–Y2=2
Q–Y UY2
A prime is beautiful to behold, but what do you do for an encore? If you unwisely make the prime, you will be forced to wreck your board or run a back man out at your next turn — and then your game is ruined.

93

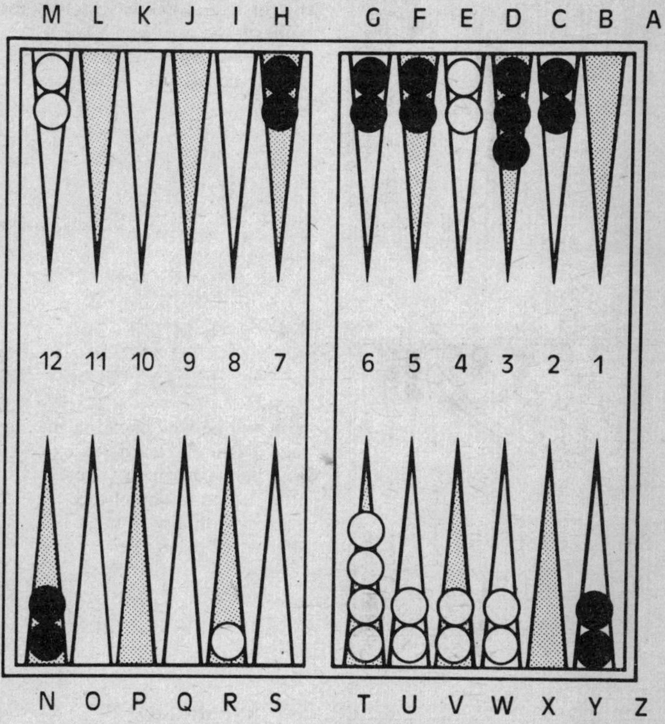

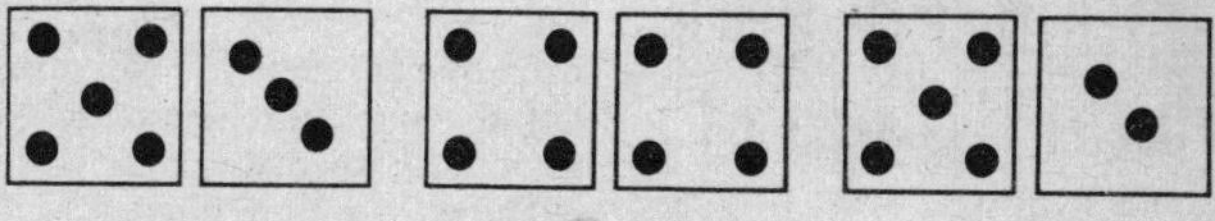

MR MP   mR[2] TX[2]   MR-MO

3   3

SCORE 8

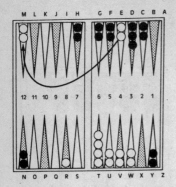

5-3   MR MP=3

E–M

This is a good time to make a run for it as Black has no way to point on the man you have left behind — unless he throws a miracle double 3.

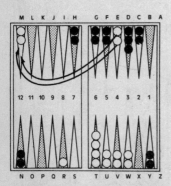

4-4   E–M TX2=3
        MQ2 TX2=2
        EI2 TX2=1

E–M2

You will be well ahead in the race if you make a quick exit with your back men. There is little reason to complicate matters with any of the alternative plays.

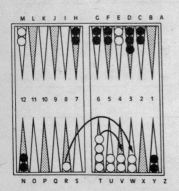

5-2   MR MO=2
        E–L=1

RW TV

There is not much you can do with this poor roll. The only attractive choice is to play safe and construct more builders.

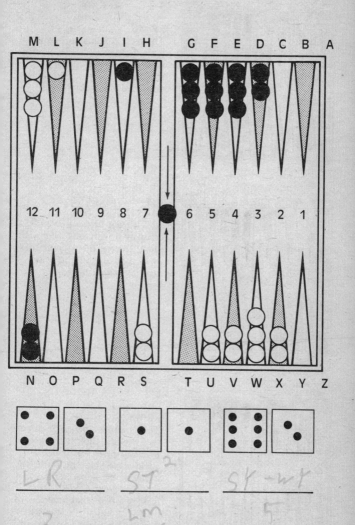

LR — ST² SY–wt

3 LM 5
NX
8

SCORE 13

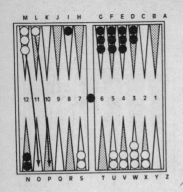

4-2   L–R=3
M–S=1

LP MO
The risk of having one of your blots hit is worth it, for you should give yourself the maximum chance at remaking your valuable 6-point.

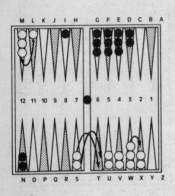

1-1   ST2 XY2=2
LM ST2 WX
This is your best roll and you can play it with total safety in mind. Even if Black enters right away, you are still the heavy favorite to win the game.

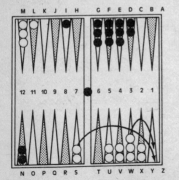

6-2   LR MO=4
L–T=1

SY WY
This is a tough play and either of the two best choices are good. Bringing down two builders could leave you a bit off-balance if you do not succeed in remaking your 6-point. By making a five-point inner board, instead, you make it much more difficult for Black to enter and, thus, that much easier for you to hustle in and win the race.

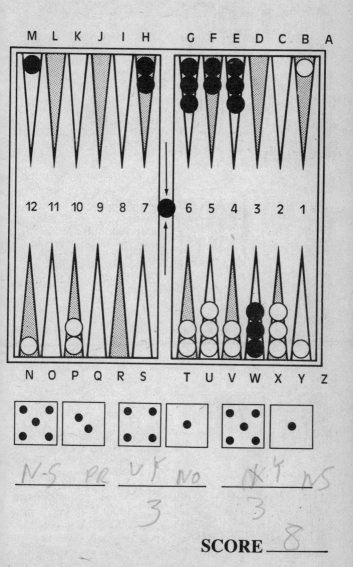

N-S PR UY NO XY NS

3 3

SCORE 8

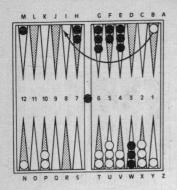

5-2   BD NS=2
          BD PU=1

B–I

The best idea is to flee your
opponent's four-point block. The
other choice of moving from
your 12-point to add a builder is
risky.

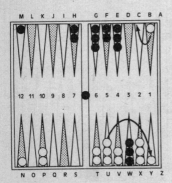

4-1   PT XY=1

BC UY

You can cover your 1-point with
either number, but by electing to
do so with the 4, you get to
move your back man one space.
Now you are in position to
vacate Black's inner board if you
throw a 6.

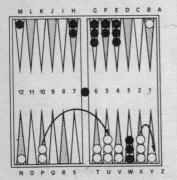

5-1   NS XY=3
          BC NS=1
          BC PU=1

PU XY

Making a five-point board is
mandatory, even at the risk of
leaving your back man stranded
on the 1-point. By playing the 5
as suggested, you do not leave a
blot that can be hit immediately
for Black is on the bar.

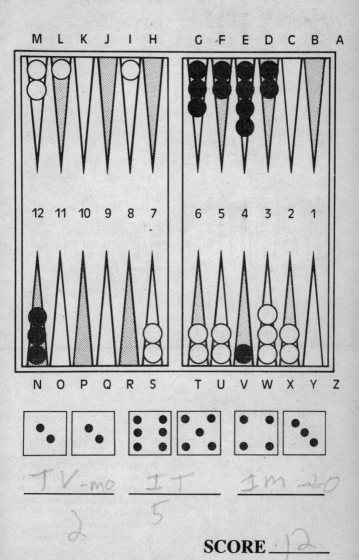

SCORE ___ 12

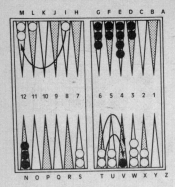

2-2 I–O WY=3
I–M SU2=1

I–M TV2'

This type of play has been nicknamed "the wash": You abandon a perfectly good point to hit your opponent and keep him busy. Black will be preoccupied with trying to enter and there will be fewer rolls for him to hit your forced blot on the 11-point.

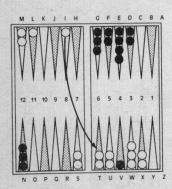

6-5 IO LQ=2
L–W=1

I–T

Moving your furthest man all the way in to safety leaves Black the fewest rolls to hit. The alternative plays are too awkward and too risky.

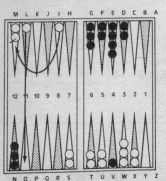

4-3 LP SV' = 2
L–S=1
IM SV'=1

IM LO

By moving as suggested, you bring one blot to safety and drop the other one down to only an indirect hit. The option of hitting Black and leaving a blot is unwise because he has an impressive four-point inner board.

ADVANCED QUIZZES

XIII
END GAME PLAYS

5?

SCORE FOR THIS SECTION _____

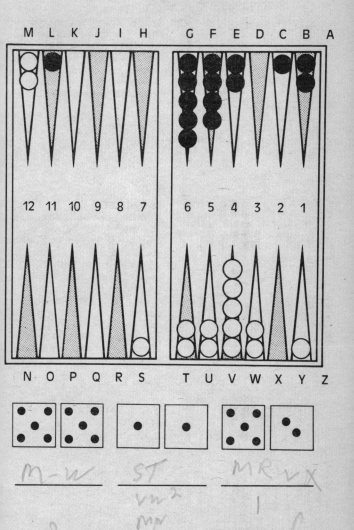

M-W   ST   MR-X
       VN2   1
       MN
2   3   SCORE __6__

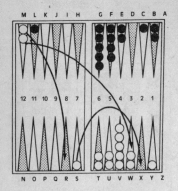

5-5 M–W2=2
M–W MR SX
To play this roll with maximum effect, you should play your last 5 to your 2-point and leave your lone man on your 8-point. Now you will have at least one man on every inside point to make bearing off that much easier.

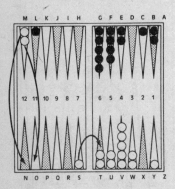

1-1 MN2 ST WX=3
M–O MN ST
By bringing a man to your 11-point, you will be able to bring him in with a 6 or 5. When you have alternatives in bearing in, placing a man on your 11-point instead of leaving it on the 12-point is much more effective as it gives you almost twice as much chance to bear in on your next roll. Playing MN2 ST WX has some merit because you do spread your men out in your inner board.

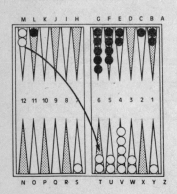

5-2 MR MO=4
MR SU=3
MR VX=1
M–T
Bearing in your remaining men as quickly and economically as possible takes priority over the other choices.

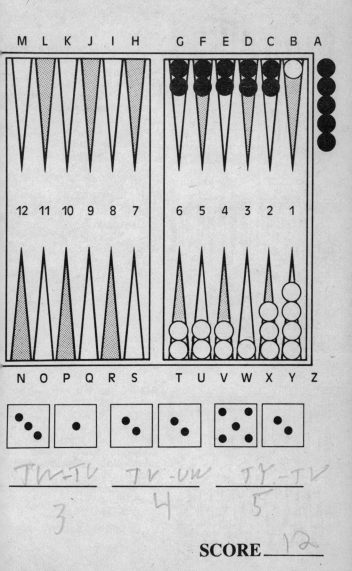

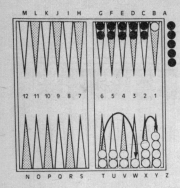

3-1   TW TU=3
         VY VW=1

TW XY

When you have to break up your inner board, the general rule is to break from the high point first. You keep a man on the 6-point so that you will have the option of staying with your back man on the 1-point if you throw a five on your next roll and Black has cleared his own 6-point.

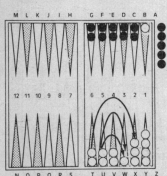

2-2   TV2 UW2=4
         UW2 VX2=1

T–X UW2

This roll is a nightmare. Remaining on the 6-point with one man may enable you to stay back on the 1-point a little longer in hopes of a desperation hit.

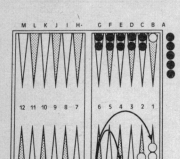

5-2   TY UW=3
         TY WY=3

TY TV

Breaking cleanly from your highest point is the general guideline to follow, although neither of the alternatives are bad plays.

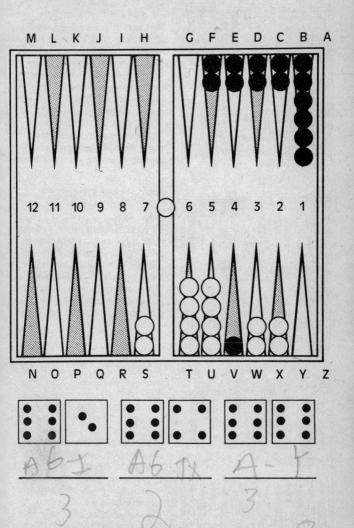

A6 I
___
3

A6 IX
___
2

A - Y
___
3

SCORE 8

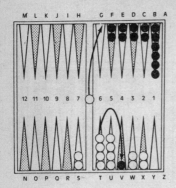

6-2   A–I=3
AG TV'
This play is preferable to running all the way with the man on the bar. By hitting, you give yourself a good chance to make a prime, although you do risk being hit and bucking a five-point inner board. Actually the only throws that could hurt you are 6-4, 5-4, or double 4, for there is a likelihood that if Black should enter, he will simultaneously have to break up his inner board.

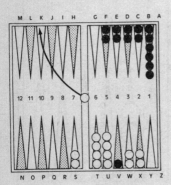

6-4   AG TX=2
AG UY=1

A–K
By running all the way, you put yourself in an excellent position to hit Black as he exits from your inner board. Furthermore, if the game turns into a straight race, you might be very happy that you chose to run as fast as you did.

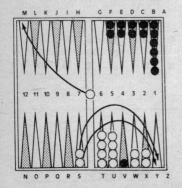

6-6   A–Y=3
A–M SY2
It is dramatic to move the maximum 24 pips with one man (A–Y), but there is a better play available: You should stop at Black's 12-point and lay in ambush in hopes of getting a hit. If you miss, you have not wasted that many pips and you will still have a chance in a running game as you have only one more man to bear in.

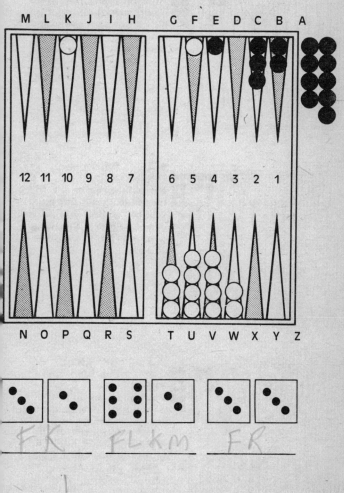

F.K   FLKM   FR

J

SCORE _____

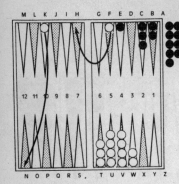

3-2 F–K=1
FH KN
No sense making your 2-point here! You have to run for your life and you must play your dice economically to avoid being gammoned.

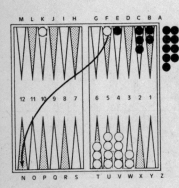

6-2 FH KQ=1
F–N
Because the man on K cannot be brought into your inner board, your best strategy is to put your other lone man in a direct position to get in from your 12-point.

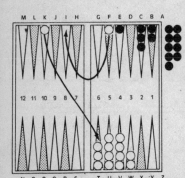

3-3 F–O KN=3
F–L KN UX=1
FI K–T
Bearing in a man to your 6- or 5-point is invariably better than bringing two men to your outer board. If you play F–O KN, you will not be able to beat the gammon with a roll of double 4, whereas you would do so if you play as suggested.

101

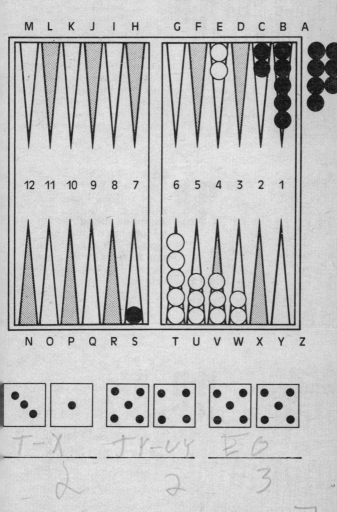

T–X   Jr–uy   EO
  2   2   3

SCORE ___ 7

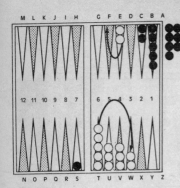

3-1

EH TU=5
EF UX=4
EH EF=2
E–I=1

EF TW

Splitting your back men is necessary to dramatically improve your odds of hitting Black's blot as he heads for home. When there is a choice of how to split, it is usually best to keep the two men close together rather than leave too wide a gap between them.

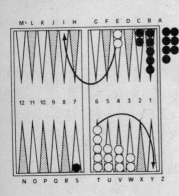

5-4

EJ TX=4
EJ EI=3
TY UY=2

EI TY

Passing up making your 1-point for splitting your back men is superior. The odds are now in your favor for getting a direct shot at Black's lone man on your next throw.

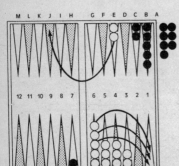

5-5

E–O TY2=3

EJ TY3

A high roll you really do not need, but this one can be put to good use. Keep a man on E in case Black throws big and gets by the man you deploy on J. Your other three men are moved en masse to the 1-point to make an impressive five-point board.

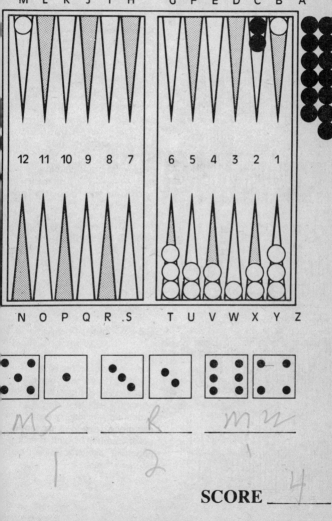

MS _____ R _____ MU

1   2

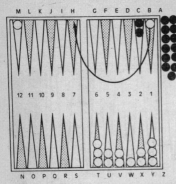

5-1 M–S=1
MR TU=1

B–H
If your opponent had three men on his 2-point, you would stay and risk the backgammon, for the chances are excellent of hitting at least one blot. However, with only two men left, it is unwise to risk the loss of a triple game by staying back and hoping for him to throw a 1.

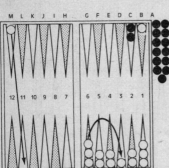

3-2 M–R=2

MO TW
Because you are unable to escape anyway, by all means make your prime and stay back for a last-ditch effort.

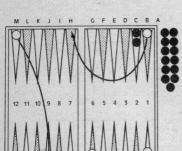

6-4 B–L=3
M–W=1

BH MQ
Making a closed board is tempting, but when your opponent has only two men remaining, the best plan is to flee and avoid a backgammon. By playing as suggested, you will avoid gammon, too, if your opponent throws a single 1 and you toss double 6.

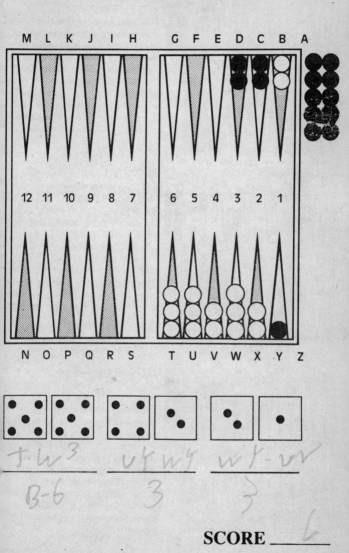

SCORE _____

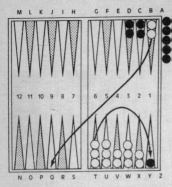

5-5 B–V=2
B–Q TY'
It is best to hit in this position as it does not matter if you are hit back. Your idea is to make it difficult for Black to run his last man around and gammon you.

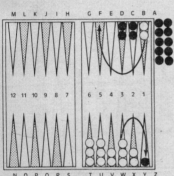

4-2 UY' WY=3
TX WY'=1
BF WY'
By all means hit but do not close your board! If you make a prime, Black will not throw and you will not have a chance to pick up another one of his men. By slotting on the 1-point, you hope he rolls 2-1 or 1-1, which will force him to expose from his four other men.

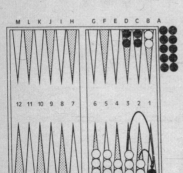

2-1 UV WY'=3
TU WY'=1
WY' XY
The best play to win the game is to try to hit a second man. If you hit and leave a blot on the 1-point, Black will use a 1 he throws to enter and he will not have to expose in his inner board. If, however, you make the unusual play of switching points, your opponent will now have to expose if he throws 2-1 himself!

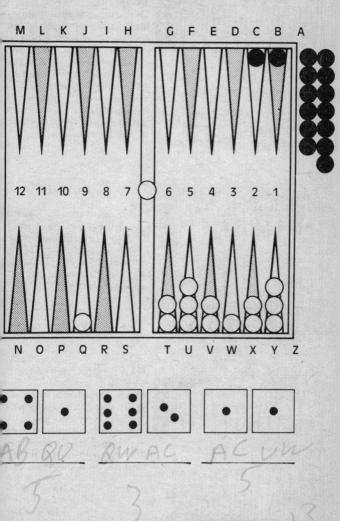

AB QU   QW AC   AC UW

5   3   5

SCORE _____ 13

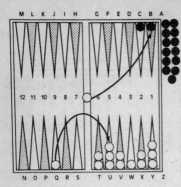

4-1   AB' UY=4
AB' QU

This position resulted from Black having three men left on his 2-point and White having one man on his 1-point. Black threw a 1 and a higher number with it, leaving a double shot. Your 4-1 roll is safely played by hitting a blot and moving in from your 9-point. You must stay back on his 1-point as you may be able to hit Black's other blot.

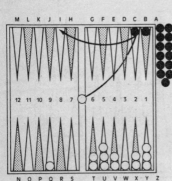

6-2   AC' QW=3
AC'I

You hit, of course, but you forgo making the prime! You want Black to hit you on the 3-point so that you get a chance of hitting his other blot. If you put two of his men on the bar, you can win the game!

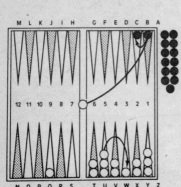

1-1   AB'C' W–Y=1
AB'C' U–W

This is a dream roll. From almost being backgammoned, you have turned the game around to the point where you have a good chance of winning it! You should eagerly hit both blots and fill in the prime.

ADVANCED QUIZZES

XIV
BEARING OFF

SCORE FOR THIS SECTION _____

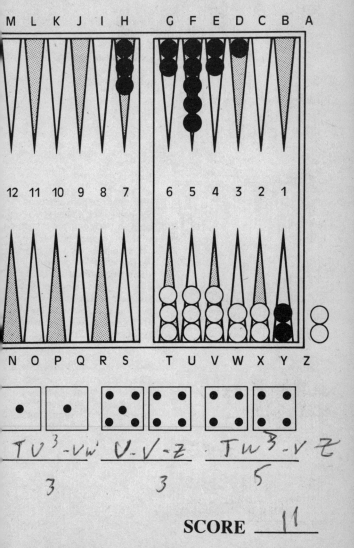

$TV^3 - VW' \quad V - V - Z \quad TW^3 - VZ$

3   3   5

SCORE 11

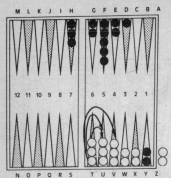

1-1 TU3 VW=3
T–V U–W=1

TU2 T–V

By making the suggested play, you will not have to leave a shot if you roll 6-4, 5-4, or 4-3 (six rolls). If you play TU3 VW, you avoid leaving a shot on only two rolls: 6-6 and 5-5.

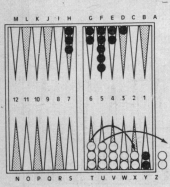

5-4 UZ VZ=3

TX UZ

When your opponent has an ace-point back game, you should keep an even number of men on your two highest points. You can accomplish this here by bearing off only one man — although a 6-5 roll at your next turn will leave a double shot. If you bear off two men, you do not risk a double shot, but there are too many rolls that will force a single shot.

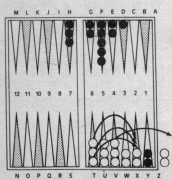

4-4 TX VZ3=2

TX3 VZ

If you bear off all from an interior point, you greatly increase the risk of leaving a shot sooner or later. Play it safe

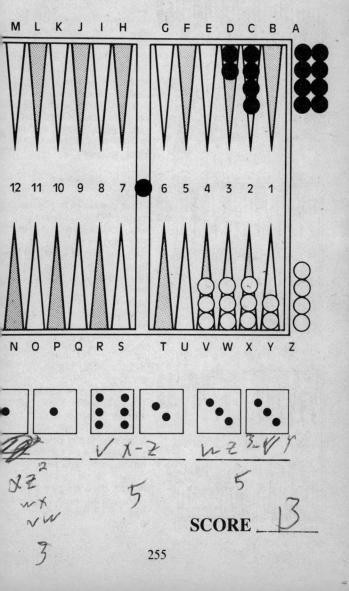

SCORE 13

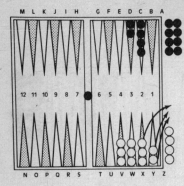

1-1
$$V-Z=2$$
$$V-X \quad VW2=1$$
X-Z YZ2

If you play safe and clear your 4-point, your opponent could win the game by entering with a throw of high doubles. You must, instead, bear off three men so that you will have a good chance of winning even if he rolls well. Also, there is little cause for worry if Black lands on your 1-point: He will be forced to vacate it if he throws a 4 or higher with his 1!

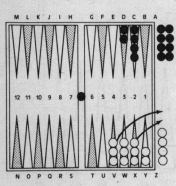

6-2
$$VZ \quad WY=2$$
VZ XZ

There is no need to play the 2 by moving WY because the only way you can leave a shot on your next throw is if your opponent fails to enter and you throw a set of doubles higher than double 2. If this should happen, you would be able to bear off three or four men and would probably win the game even if you were hit.

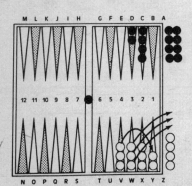

3-3
$$VY3 \quad WZ=3$$
VY WZ3

You have to bear off three men. If your opponent enters on the 3-point, he will have to exit from there unless his throw is 3-1. The odds on him doing this and you leaving a shot and him hitting you — and you losing the race — are very great indeed. By bearing off three men, you are in good shape to win even if Black throws high numbers.

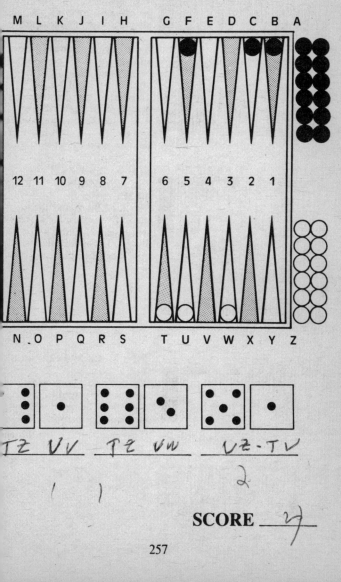

TZ VV   TZ VW   VZ-TV

2

SCORE 4

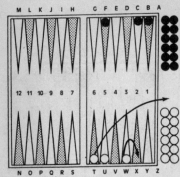

6-1   TZ UV=2
TZ WX

Your opponent is almost sure to get off in two rolls, so you must play to also get all remaining men off on your next turn. By leaving two men on the 5-point and 2-point, it will be easier to bear off than leaving two men on the 4-point and 3-point.

To avoid memorizing tables on bearing off, the general rule is to move the lower man when two are left — except if one of the men is on the 6-point.

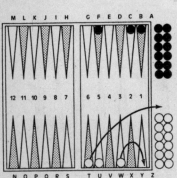

6-2   TV UZ=1
           TZ UW=1
TZ WY

Play the 2 by moving the lower man. If you move the higher man, you will double up on the 3-point. In bearing off, spread your men when there is a choice.

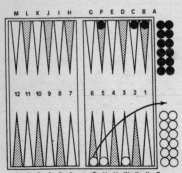

5-1   UZ WX=2
T–Z

The 5 presents no problem and the 1 is best played by moving from the higher point whenever the 6-point is involved.

108

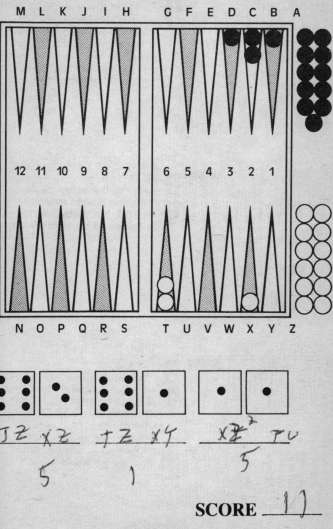

JZ XZ   TZ XY   XZ² TU
  5   1   5

SCORE 11

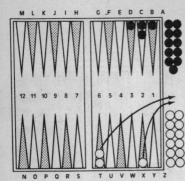

6-2   TZ TV=1
TZ XZ
Bearing off the maximum number of men in situations such as this is invariably better and this case is no exception. It will be much easier to bear off one man from your 6-point on your next roll than two men from the 4-point and 2-point.

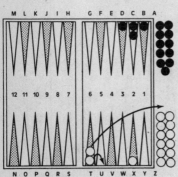

6-1   TZ XY=1
TZ TU
The exception to moving the lower man is when the 6-point is involved. You should play the 1 by moving off the highest point.

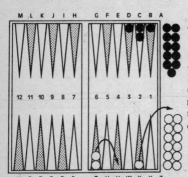

1-1
T–V X–Z
"Bear off whatever you can and spread what remains" is the rule of thumb to follow. Here it will be easier to bear off from the 6-point and 4-point than two men from the 5-point — although the odds are against you getting off in one roll in either case.

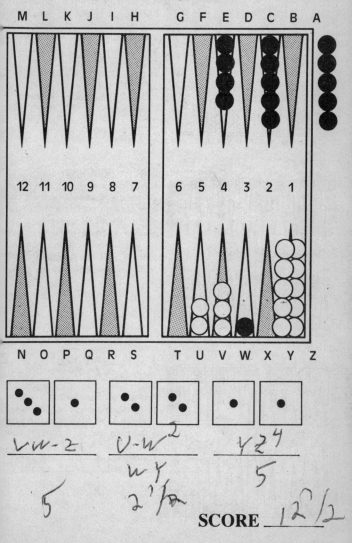

VW-2

V-W²

YZ4

WY

5

2½

5

SCORE 12½

109

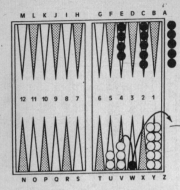

3-1   VYZ=2
VW'Z

You could bear off without hitting, but by putting your opponent on the bar, you give yourself a better chance to win what could wind up being a close race. Now he will be farther back by three pips and there is an additional chance that he may be unlucky and not even enter right away.

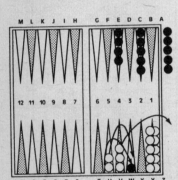

2-2   V–Z VX2=1
UW2' V–Z

Because you cannot bear off two men without leaving a shot, you might as well be aggressive and pounce on Black's blot. You still are able to bear off one man and there is a chance he may throw badly and not enter on his next roll.

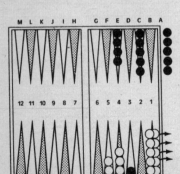

1-1   VW3' YZ=2
               VW'–Z=1
YZ4

Bearing off four men is too good to resist. Now you are the heavy favorite to win the race and your liability in leaving a shot on your next roll is nil, for if Black throws a 4 or higher with either die, he will be forced to exit!

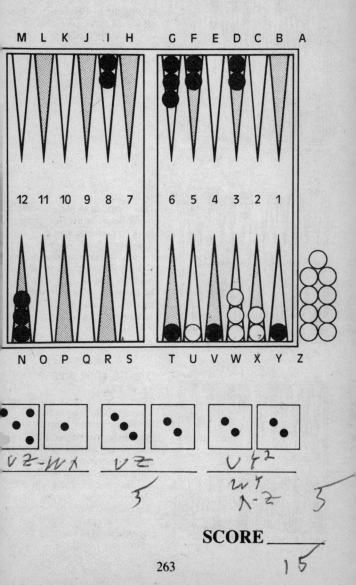

SCORE

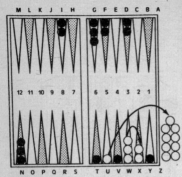

5-1   UV' Z=2
UZ WX
Hitting the blot and then bearing off would make your chances for scoring a triple game less remote but would severely reduce your odds on winning a gammon or even the game itself. Here the safe play predominates over the fancy hit-and-run option.

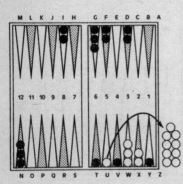

3-2   UX WY'=2
U–Z
It is tempting to play UX WY', but if Black throws a 1 to hit you back, it could be a long, drawn-out game in which you eventually see your chances for scoring a gammon dwindle to nothing. The better policy is to be content to win a probable gammon by making the conservative play.

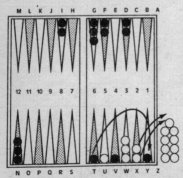

2-2   U–Y' WY2=3
U–Y' XZ2
Here is one of the few situations where it is worth the risk of losing a gammon in order to go for all the marbles — a backgammon! By bearing off two men, you leave yourself with only four pieces; if Black does not hit your blot, you will win the triple game by throwing double 3 or better or by bearing off in two turns if Black is unsuccessful in escaping from your inner board.

111

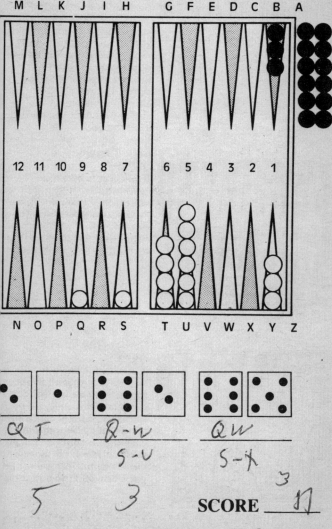

QT   Q-W   QW
      S-V   S-X

5   3   SCORE 17

265

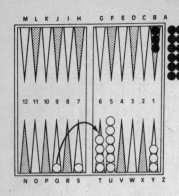

2-1   S–V=2
Q–T
You should bear in so you will be able to bear off and avert gammon on your next turn — unless your opponent throws doubles and that is an event that you have no control over. The recommended play will achieve your goal unless you subsequently roll 3-2, 4-2, or double 4; if you play alternatively, you will not be able to bear off if you roll 3-2, 4-2, 5-2, or 6-2.

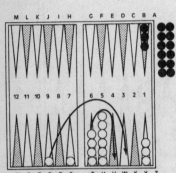

6-2   QW SU=3
QW TV
If you bear in both men, you will be embarrassed if you subsequently throw double 4. Playing as suggested gets you a man off on your next turn no matter what you throw next.

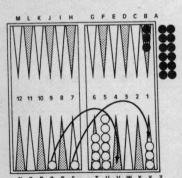

6-5   QW SX=3
QV SY
The rule of thumb is to bear in so as to give yourself maximum spread, but here is a weird exception! If you play 6-5 by spreading, you will not be able to bear off a man with a throw double 4. If, however, you play the paradoxical way as shown, there is no roll that will not get you a man off at your next turn

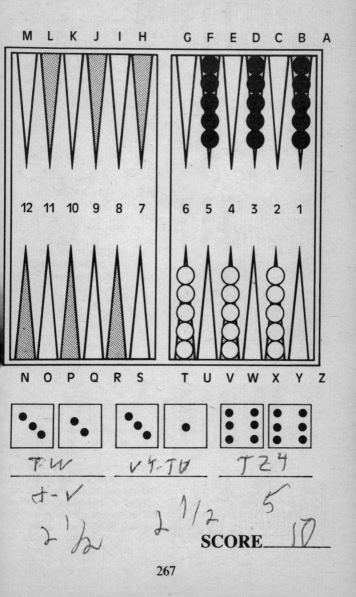

TW

VY TU   JZY

T-V

2 1/2   2 1/2   5

SCORE 10

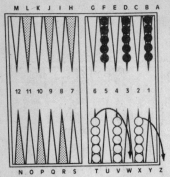

3-2   VY XZ=3

TW XZ

This last situation would be very unlikely to occur in an actual game, but it will give you practice in bearing-off techniques. The play of the 3 of this roll is difficult, but it is a good technique to clear men off the 6-point.

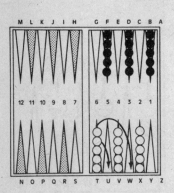

3-1   TW XY=5
         V-Z=4

TW TU

Admittedly this is a tough choice. By spreading, however, you unpile your men and the remainder of the bearing-off process should be easier.

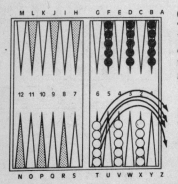

6-6

TZ4

Well played. If you missed this one, you are in trouble! Actually this setup is a charming little game in itself: The player with 6-4-2 rolls first. and the doubling cube is in play and starts in the middle. (Alternate opening setups if you play more than one game.) The player bearing off first wins and you will be surprised at how close the results are — and how high the cube can be turned!

APPENDIX

SUGGESTED WAYS TO PLAY THE OPENING ROLLS

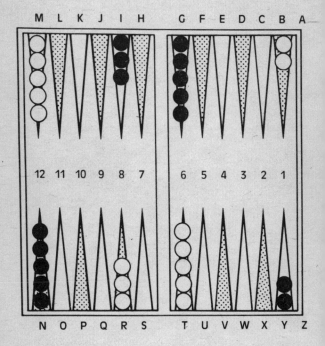

ROLL	SUGGESTED PLAY	ALTERNATIVE PLAY
Pointing Plays		
3-1	RU TU	_____
6-1	MS RS	_____
4-2	RV TV	MQ MO
Running Plays		
6-5	B–M	_____
6-4	B–L	BH MQ
6-3	B–K	BH MP
Slotting Plays		
6-2	M–U	BH MO
5-1	MR TU	BC MR
4-1	MQ TU	BC MQ
2-1	MO TU	BC MO
Twin-Builder Plays		
4-3	MQ MP	BE MQ
3-2	MP MO	BE MO
Single-Builder Plays		
5-4	MR MQ	B–K
5-3	MR MP	RW TW
5-2	MR MO	_____
Doubles		
6-6	BH2 MS2	_____
5-5	M–W2	_____
4-4	BF2 MQ2	M–U2
3-3	RU2 TW2	M–S2
2-2	MO2 TV2	B–F2
1-1	RS2 TU2	_____

DICE COMBINATIONS

With all the pairs of doubles, there is only one combination of each:

1. 6-6 
2. 5-5 
3. 4-4 
4. 3-3 
5. 2-2 
6. 1-1

Total: Six possible rolls

With all the pairs of nondoubles, there are two combinations of each:

1. 6-5, 5-6
2. 6-4, 4-6
3. 6-3, 3-6

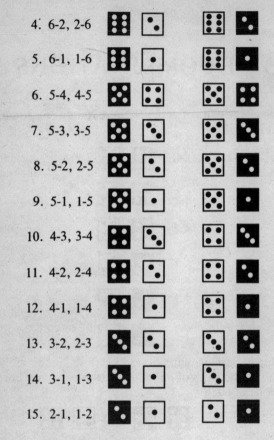

4. 6-2, 2-6

5. 6-1, 1-6

6. 5-4, 4-5

7. 5-3, 3-5

8. 5-2, 2-5

9. 5-1, 1-5

10. 4-3, 3-4

11. 4-2, 2-4

12. 4-1, 1-4

13. 3-2, 2-3

14. 3-1, 1-3

15. 2-1, 1-2

Total: 30 possible rolls
Grand Total: 36 possible rolls

PROBABILITY TABLES

CHART I–PROBABILITY OF ENTERING FROM THE BAR

No. of Points Open	One Man on Bar		Two Men on Bar (probability of both entering)	
	Ways to Come In	Chances of Coming In	Ways to Come In	Chances of Coming In
6	36	100%	36	100%
5	35	97%	25	69%
4	32	89%	16	44%
3	27	75%	9	25%
2	20	56%	4	11%
1	11	31%	1	3%
0	0	0%	0	0%

CHART II–PROBABILITY OF HITTING A BLOT

(This chart does not take into consideration any points made by the opponent that are situated between you and the blot.)

Number of Points Away	Ways to be Hit	Chances of Being Hit	Number of Points Away	Ways to be Hit	Chances of Being Hit
1	11	31%	13,14	0	0%
2	12	33%	15	1	3%
3	14	39%	16	1	3%
4	15	42%	17	0	0%
5	15	42%	18	1	3%
6	17	47%	19	0	0%
7	6	17%	20	1	3%
8	6	17%	21,22,23	0	0%
9	5	14%	24	1	3%
10	3	8%			
11	2	6%			
12	3	8%			

CHART III–PROBABILITY OF BEARING OFF THE LAST ONE OR TWO MEN IN ONE ROLL

Point or Points Occupied	Ways to Get Off in One Roll	Chances of Getting Off
1	36	100%
2	36	100%
1,1	36	100%
3	36	100%
2,1	36	100%
4	34	94%
3,1	34	94%
5	31	86%
4,1	29	81%
6	27	75%
2,2	26	72%
3,2	25	69%
5,1	23	64%
4,2	23	64%
5,2	19	53%
3,3	17	47%
4,3	17	47%
6,1	15	42%
5,3	14	39%
6,2	13	36%
4,4	11	31%
6,3	10	28%
5,4	10	28%
6,4	8	22%
5,5	6	17%
6,5	6	17%
6,6	4	11%

RULES
FOR PLAYING
BACKGAMMON

1. **PLAYERS:** The game of backgammon is played by two players who sit opposite each other.

2. **EQUIPMENT:** One player has 15 pieces (*men*) of one color and the other player has 15 pieces of another color. Each player has a *dice cup* and two standard *dice*. The *backgammon board* has four quadrants (*tables*) each of which has six triangles (*points*), and the points on the board are alternately colored. The strip bisecting the middle of the board is called the *bar*.

BLACK

OPPONENT'S OUTER TABLE   OPPONENT'S INNER TABLE

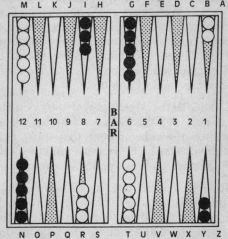

YOUR OUTER TABLE   YOUR INNER TABLE

WHITE

277

3. **SETUP:** The men are set up on the board as shown with White moving his men in a counterclockwise direction and Black moving in a clockwise direction. The position of the men may be reversed or the board may be set up so that the inner tables are on the left side instead of the right side (a mirror image of the diagram above). For ease of discussion, the points of the board are numbered as follows: each player's six inner-board points are numbered 1 to 6 and his outer-board points are numbered 7 to 12.

4. **PRELIMINARIES:** Before the first game, a player chooses his color men, the direction his men will move and his seat at the table. If the opposing player wishes the same color men, or the same direction or seat, the players roll one die each and the player rolling the higher number has his choice of men, direction and seat, and such is not changed for the duration of play.

5. **DICE:** At the start of play or before the start of any game, a player may ask that the dice be mixed. One player then takes all four dice, shakes them in his cup and throws them on the board. The opponent takes one die of his choice, then the player takes one die, then the opponent takes his second die and then the player takes the last die. The dice for backgammon should be accurately fabricated and may be either square-cornered or round-cornered and of any color.

6. **OPENING ROLL:** Each player throws a single die from his cup into the half-board at his right. If the players throw the same number, they throw again. The player throwing the higher number goes first and moves both his number and his opponent's number.

7. **THROWING THE DICE:** After the first turn, a player uses both dice for his roll. He puts the dice into his dice cup, shakes them thoroughly and throws them into the half-board at his right. The dice must come to rest flat in the right half-board or else the dice are "cocked" and must be rethrown. The dice are also

278

cocked when either or both dice land atop a man, lean at an angle against a wall of the board or a man, land on an edge or fall one on top of the other.

8. A COMPLETED PLAY: A player's turn is over after he moves his men and picks up his dice. Only when both dice are removed from the board may his opponent throw and move; if the opponent throws before the player's dice are up, the player may require his opponent to throw again.

9. MOVING: A play is made by moving a man the same number of points as the number appearing on a die. For example, if a player's roll is a 6 and 3, he would move one of his men six points and another three points, or he would move one man nine points, the total of the two dice. (See Diagrams B and C.)

DIAGRAM B

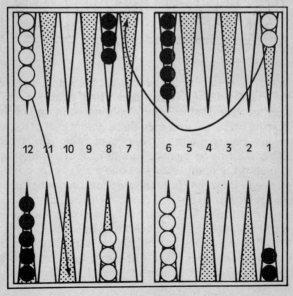

279

DIAGRAM C

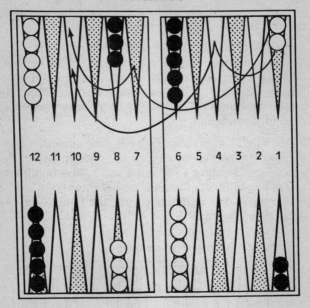

When the numbers on the dice are the same, a player moves the number four times. For example, if a player's roll is double 3, he would move in any of the following ways: (a) four men three points each; (b) two men six points each; (c) one man nine points and another man three points; (d) one man six points and two men three points each; (e) one man twelve points.

A player must play both the numbers on his dice if it is possible for him to do so. For example, in Diagram D if a player rolls 6-2, he must play his move as shown for there is no other way to play a 6 in this situation. If a player is able to move both numbers on the dice, he may move either number first. If he can move either of the two numbers but is unable to move both of them, he must move the higher number.

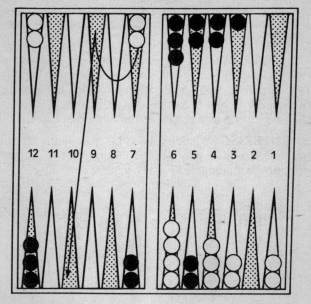

If a player is able to move only one of the numbers shown, he moves that number and the turn to play passes to the opponent. If he throws doubles and cannot play the number rolled four times but can play it one, two, or three times, he does so and his turn is completed. If a player can move neither number, he does not move and it is his opponent's turn to play.

10. **POINTS:** When a player has two or more men on a triangle, it is a *point* and an opponent's man may not occupy or touch down on that space.

A player may have any number of men occupy one of his points, but once the number is more than five or six, any additional men should be stacked so that they will not reach over to the triangle directly across the board.

11. **PRIMES:** When a player succeeds in making six consecutive points anywhere on the board, it is called a *prime* and the opponent is blocked completely from moving past them.

12. **BLOTS:** When a player has only one man on a triangle, such a man is called a *blot* and the opponent is free to play to that space. If a man lands on a space occupied by a blot of an opponent, the blot is *hit* and is then picked up and placed in the middle of the bar.

13. **ENTERING:** When a man is hit, it remains on the bar and is out of play until it can be entered in the opponent's inner table by a throw of the dice. To enter a

DIAGRAM E

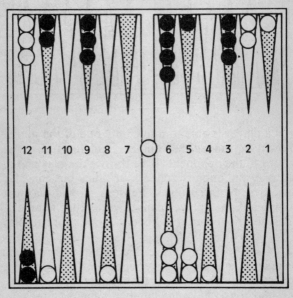

man from the bar, a player must throw a number on one of the dice that corresponds to any point not blocked by the opponent in his inner table. For example, the man on the bar in Diagram E cannot enter on a throw of 6-3, double 6 or double 3; it can enter on 1,2,4 or 5. If the man enters on 1, the blot there is converted to a point; if it enters on 2, it lands on a point already possessed; if it comes in on 4, it makes a blot; if it enters on 5, it hits a blot sending the opponent's man to the bar.

A player having a man or men on the bar may not play any other man until such man or men on the bar have entered.

When a player has a prime in his inner table, his opponent does not throw the dice if he has a man on the bar for such man could not enter regardless of what throw is made.

14. **BEARING OFF:** When a player has all 15 of his men in his inner table, he uses his dice rolls to bring his men off the board (*bearing off*). The men that are borne off are removed and stacked or piled up off the board.

When a player is in a position to bear off, he bears off a man from a point corresponding to the number on a die thrown, or bears off from the highest occupied point that is lower than the number shown on a die. For example, in Diagram F, White plays a 6-4 roll by bearing off from the 5-point (the highest occupied point) and from the 4-point. If a player can bear off or move a man forward within, he may do either play. To illustrate, in Diagram F, White can play a roll of 5-3 by: (a) bearing off a man from the 5-point and a man from the 3-point; (b) bearing off from the 5-point and moving a man from the 4-point to the 1-point; (c) moving from the 5-point to the 2-point and then playing the 5 by bearing off from the 4-point.

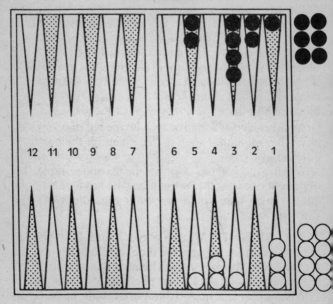

If a man is hit while in the process of bearing off, it must be entered and moved around the board into the inner table before bearing off is resumed.

A player may play either number first in bearing off. Thus, in the position shown in Diagram G, a roll of 6-1 could be played by White by moving the 1 first to the 5-point and then bearing off the same man. (If, instead, the 6 were played first, a blot would have to be left in moving the 1.)

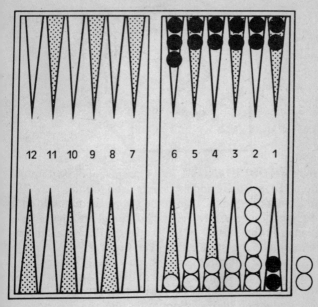

15. **WINNING THE GAME:** The game is won by the player who first bears off all his men. If the loser is able to bear off at least one of his men, the winner is awarded a single game. If the loser has not been able to bear off at least one man, it is a *gammon* and scores a double game for the winner. If the loser has not borne off a man and has one or more men stranded in his opponent's inner table or on the bar, it is a *backgammon* and scores a triple game for the winner.

16. **THE DOUBLING CUBE:** The special die with numbers 2, 4, 8, 16, 32 and 64 on it is used to raise the stake or points of a game. (On some cubes the number 64 is replaced by 1.) After the start of the game, the cube is placed in the middle of the bar or off the board to one side an equal distance from each player.

After the opening roll has been played, either player may double the stake when it is his turn before he throws the dice. When he doubles, he turns the cube to 2 and places it on the opponent's side and may accompany this action by saying "Double."

The opponent decides either to accept or refuse the double. A refusal of a double terminates the game and the player declining loses whatever the unit was before the double was made. The pieces are then set up anew and the next game is begun.

If the opponent accepts, the game continues for double the stake and the doubler then throws his dice and play resumes. After a double is accepted, the player who doubled cannot make the next double, for the cube is on the side of the player who accepted. That player may redouble (turn the cube to 4) anytime it is his turn before he rolls his dice. If he decides to do so, he turns the cube to the next higher number and places it on his opponent's side. If the opponent accepts, the stake is now doubled again.

A gammon doubles and a backgammon triples whatever number is shown on the cube.

When a player has a prime in his inner board and his opponent has one or more men on the bar, although the opponent does not roll his dice, he may still double when it is his turn.

If both players agree beforehand, when each throws the same number for his opening roll, it is an automatic double and the doubling cube is turned from 1 (64) to 2 but is left in the middle. If the players again throw the same number, the cube is left on 2 unless the players have already agreed to play a second automatic double.

17. **IRREGULARITIES:** (1) If the men are set up incorrectly, such error must be corrected if either player notices it before the second player plays his second turn. After this, the incorrect setup stands. If a player starts with fewer than 15 men and the error is not discovered until after the second player has played his second turn, such man or men that are off the board are deemed to be on the bar. (2) If an error in play has been made, either player may require its correction before a subsequent roll. A player may correct his error by replaying his entire move if he wishes.

ABOUT THE AUTHOR

Prince Joli Kansil is the inventor of Bridgette, the two-handed bridge game, and several other nationally marketed games. He has constructed numerous crossword puzzles for *The New York Times* and other publications, is the backgammon editor of *Games* magazine, and is the author of *Backgammon!,* a book for beginning backgammon players. A teacher and world traveler as well, Prince Kansil is the founder and director of the Honolulu Backgammon Club and has participated successfully in tournaments in Europe and the Far East. He currently lives in Honolulu with his wife and daughter.